W9-BUO-850

#94

THE PIONEER CATALOGUE OF COUNTRY LIVING

THE PIONEER CATALOGUE
OF COUNTRY LIVING

—— ELMO STOLL / MARK STOLL ——

PERSONAL LIBRARY PUBLISHERS

Toronto, Canada

Personal Library, Publishers
Suite 439
17 Queen Street East
Toronto, Canada M5C 1P9

Publisher: *Glenn Edward Witmer*
Editor: *Ex Libris/Charis Wahl*
Production Editor: *Catherine Van Baren*
Design: *Design Collaborative Ltd.*
Cover Design: *First Image/Michael Gray*
Line Illustrations: *Paul Weldon*
Assembly: *Katija Mohideen*
Composition: *CompuScreen Typesetting Ltd.*

Distributed to the trade by
John Wiley and Sons Canada Limited
22 Worcester Road
Rexdale, Ontario M9W 1L1

Canadian Cataloguing in Publication Data

Stoll, Elmo, 1944-
   The pioneer catalogue of country living

Includes index.
ISBN 0-920510-13-2

1. Country life—Handbooks, manuals, etc.
2. Home economics, Rural—Handbooks, manuals, etc.
3. Implements, utensils, etc.—Catalogs.
I. Stoll, Mark, 1952—. II. Title.

TX147.S81   640′.4   C80-094354-6

Printed and bound in Canada

Contents

Preface   *ix*

Introduction: Simple Living   *11*

Part One: On the Land

Chapter 1: Free as the Wind   *20*

Chapter 2: Horse Power   *23*

Chapter 3: Out of Doors   *31*

Chapter 4: Martins, Mice and Mosquitos   *33*

Chapter 5: The Apple Orchard   *43*

Chapter 6: Grow Your Own Cow   *45*

Chapter 7: A Ringing Message   *59*

Part Two: Home

Chapter 8: Warm Friends   *63*

Chapter 9: Common-Sense Canning   *67*

Chapter 10: The Butcher   *80*

Chapter 11: And the Baker   *83*

Chapter 12: Things I Want My Daughter to Learn   *87*

Chapter 13: Through the Mill   *94*

Chapter 14: How to Cheat the Grocery Man   *96*

Chapter 15: Let There Be Light   *100*

Chapter 16: The Comforts of Home   *103*

Acknowledgements

Grateful acknowledgement is made to the following persons for permission to incorporate into our text material they provided:

To Elizabeth Miller, Aylmer, Ontario, for the use of "Common Sense Canning" in Chapter 9.

To Joseph Stoll, Aylmer, Ontario, for the use of "The Purple Martin–Our Most Wanted Bird" in Chapter 4.

To Mrs. Ian Shantz, Wallenstein, Ontario, for the use of "Things I Want My Daughter to Learn" in Chapter 12.

To Mrs. Daniel Miller, Jr., Salem, Indiana, for help with the butter-making directions in Chapter 6.

To Mrs. Lester F. Graber, Beebe, Arkansas, for "How I Learned to Enjoy Baking Bread" in Chapter 11.

To Mrs. Martha Z. Weaver, Lititz, Pennsylvania, for "We Changed Our Minds" in Chapter 11.

To Daniel Miller, Jr., Salem, Indiana, for "The Butcher" in Chapter 10.

To Jo Ann Gardner, Orangedale, Nova Scotia, for "A Tale of Self-Reliance" in Chapter 3.

To Dr. H. Clair Amstutz, Goshen, Indiana, for much of the information on the history of breakfast cereals, used in Chapter 14.

Preface

The man was visibly upset as he drove into our lane. Even before he was out of his car, he was waving a copy of *Harrowsmith* and sputtering indignantly, "Imagine! Advertising in the country's most popular magazine, and you don't put up a sign!"

He was not the first to complain about how hard we are to find. A few days earlier a man had searched for two hours before he located "Pioneer Place." He offered to stay and help us paint a few signs. "You have to have a sign at the road," he insisted. "How do you expect people to find you?"

Well, we don't expect people to find us. We're not exactly hiding, but neither do we want a line of cars parked in the laneway. A show room, where customers could browse, might make good business sense, but we don't want to turn our home into a public store. We are two Amish families who wish to preserve our values in a quiet home life. So we do our business by mail order; our catalogue is our show room.

This catalogue came into being for two reasons. We found that many people outside our society honestly wanted some of the self-sufficiency we take for granted, but did not know where to obtain the means. We felt we could provide a service to those outside our way of life by making available some of the self-help tools we use every day.

As well, the high price of farmland is forcing our community to develop cottage industries producing hand-made furniture, harnesses, etc. Pioneer Place seeks to establish markets and retail the products of these home shops. Our community puts great emphasis on home-centered, family-oriented occupations. We do not feel it is good for a family to have the father, let alone the mother, working away from home, leaving children unattended and untrained.

So please forgive us for not having a sign at the road. Or a telephone, for that matter. We are content to do business by mail.

We do our best to keep all stock items on hand for prompt shipment, but this is not always possible. Because some of our goods are produced in limited quantities and many are hand crafted, we must sometimes ask our customers to wait. However, we will cheerfully refund your money at any time if you feel the waiting time is unreasonable.

We have worked hard to find some of the items listed in this catalogue. In fact, for some of them we could not find sources, and we have ended up manufacturing them ourselves. We could find sources for other items; but those sources were outside of Canada, and we rebelled at the outrageous price we would have had to ask you to pay. The exchange on the dollar and import duty push the cost up beyond reason. So, in the case of such things as our cider press, we had items manufactured here in Canada especially for our catalogue. We feel it has been well worth the extra effort to be able to offer a superior product at a lower price.

With inflation being ever-present in today's economy, we are not including exact prices in this catalogue. Instead, we have listed an approximate price range as a general guide. Please write to us for a complete list of current prices on all the items in this catalogue before ordering. The price list will be sent to you promptly without charge, along with order blanks and information on how we ship goods to you directly and conveniently.

In conclusion, we trust you will find this catalogue helpful. It will please us if it can help you to become less dependent on technology. Many people are discovering the satisfaction of becoming more self-sufficient; if you are not already among them, we hope you will soon be.

Best wishes from all of us,

Elmo	Solomon
Elizabeth	Mark
Caleb	Dora
Jonathan	Abigail
Andrew	Rhoda
Aaron	Dorcas

For your free copy of our current price list, write to: The Pioneer Place, Route 4, Aylmer, Ontario, Canada N5H 2R3

Simple Living

The Urban Refugee

Bill stood studying the Toronto skyline. The rising full moon shimmered in full splendor in the space between two apartment towers. Then it disappeared, hidden by glass and concrete. "That's it," Bill muttered. "There has to be a better way."

For days Bill had been brooding. He was frightened by his utter dependence on technology. He was convinced that some day people were going to be caught in a crisis without basic survival skills, and he was determined not to be one of them.

Bill began by sorting out his basic needs: water, heat, light, food. Suppose something knocked out the main electricity-generating stations. Most of the country would grind to a shuddering halt. Bill shuddered, too. How many of his basic needs could be filled if the electric power failed?

Water? Gone. All the water in the city was dependent on electricity. Heat? His apartment was electrically heated. Light? He didn't even own a candle. That left him in a cold dark room. Food? He cooked on an electric stove, so he would have to eat uncooked food. Worse yet, his freezer would go off, so his supplies would spoil. Restaurants would be in the same state, cold and dark. And to get to one, he would have to walk down 27 flights of stairs, and up them again to get back home.

So Bill joined the growing number of urban refugees, in search of a way of life that would give him a better chance. He bought a house in the country; his wife learned to can food and grow a garden. Bill is studying solar heat and wind power. His house is heated by a wood-burning stove, fueled by his own wood lot. He is not totally independent and never will be. But he is approaching the point where he would not only survive, but live fairly comfortably should that all-important electric current fade out.

Few people are willing to become urban refugees like Bill. But they are bothered by the same possibility: how they would cope, should the technological gadgets around them fail?

Fortunately, the solution does not have to be absolute in order to be of value. The person who grows a garden is better off than the person who does not, even if he still is dependent on technology for the other basics. The person who heats his house from his own wood lot is better off than the person who does not, even if he is still dependent on technology for water, light, and food.

We can take the first step if we do not let ourselves be overwhelmed by the hopelessness of obtaining absolute self-sufficiency; it was not possible, even in grandfather's day. Self-sufficiency is not like a town on a map; it is more like a road. We start out, we travel along it. We hope to make progress, to travel farther than we have so far. But we never arrive.

It is not where we are on that road that is important, but in which direction we are travelling, and with how much speed. The problem is finding the road. For so long, few people have travelled it. Many of the markers are gone, and it is overgrown in spots by thorns and brambles.

This book is not the road. It is only a rough map to that road. We realize it is not complete, but we hope that what there is of it will be clear and legible, and will guide you at least part of the way toward greater self-sufficiency.

Today we live in a time of education and scientific discovery unparalleled in history. But so much of our knowledge is specialized knowledge. There are doctors today who know more about the inner ear or a valve in the heart than any man has known since the world began. But they may know less about all-round health care than the general practitioner of grandfather's day.

This specializing of knowledge contains many inherent dangers. A person may know how to program a complicated computer, but he may be helpless when the kitchen faucet starts to leak. A brilliant heart surgeon may be unable to diagnose an elementary mechanical problem in his car.

A generation ago, few people possessed the highly specialized knowledge in their particular fields that many have today. But everyone possessed more general basic survival skills–they knew how to cope with a crisis, and how to obtain the basics of life.

Sometimes I am appalled by people's ignorance about everyday things any six-year-old in our Amish society would know. Take, for example, butter-making. A lady wrote for information on a churn. "I am assuming I can use ordinary whole milk in the churn."

Well, it is possible, of course; but since milk as it comes from the average cow is only about 3.5 per cent butterfat, her yield from a churn of milk might be enough butter for two slices of toast. Provided she could find it in all that buttermilk.

Then there was the man and his wife who realized that cream, not milk, was needed, but they didn't know when to stop churning. They thought they were supposed to churn until all the cream had changed to butter, not realizing that they would also be left with buttermilk for baking.

But I discovered, rather disconcertingly, that ignorance isn't confined to butter-making. One day I drove to town to do some shopping. Instead of tying at my usual hitching post, the hydro pole in the town parking lot, I tied my horse to a parking meter across from the bank. I wanted to put a nickel into the meter, but I couldn't figure out how to do it. The longer I searched, the more foolish I felt. That slot had to be somewhere–I had often seen motorists put in a coin–but where was it?

Finally, a lady coming down the street kindly told me to look on the sidewalk side of the meter, not on the street side. That lady went down in my books as one of today's great heroes, not because she stopped to help me, for that was a small matter, but because she possessed the self-restraint to keep a perfectly straight face in the presence of such woeful ignorance!

Ever since that day, I have been a bit slower to label other people ignorant, just because they have not yet had the opportunity to learn the things I have learned. All of us know only what our limited experience has exposed us to. Sharing our knowledge, with kindness and understanding, would be true learning.

Today, there are a lot of people interested in learning some of the skills and knowledge an earlier generation abandoned in favor of book learning. In our parents' day, country people were considered backward and unfortunate, while people in the city were the ones to be envied. Today, thousands and even millions of people in large urban centers dream of escaping from their prisons of glass and concrete. They envy people who till the soil, grow a garden, cut their own firewood, or bake their own bread.

People are fed up with chemicals and plastics and artificial things. They want things that are old, solid, proven, lasting, real. From this desire to be more self-sufficient has sprung a new class–so new it doesn't really have a name yet. We have been calling these people urban refugees; others call them homesteaders or back-to-the-landers. Whatever they are called, they are people who dream of getting back to what their grandparents dreamed of getting away from.

Many people today are adrift. They have lost their bearings in a churning sea of change and moral permissiveness. They find themselves drawn to cultures, customs, and tools of a past age, in which they can see something anchored, something constant and stable. But old things and old ways are not enough.

We, the Amish, believe in simple living, self-sufficiency and separation from the cash economy, not so that we may have food when others do not, but because we believe such a life-style is most conducive to the spiritual values we cherish. Our simple living is not an end in itself, but a means of strengthening family, church and community bonds.

Look beyond the buggies and the beards to the spiritual values we hold dear, and which we feel can best be maintained in a non-technological setting. We are not clinging to the past—we are preparing for an eternal future. The true meaning of our way of life is that it leads us closer to Jesus, the source of Life itself.

The man—we will call him Amos Beiler—was dismayed by the events that brought him to where he had never expected to be—behind bars in a Pennsylvania jail. He had always been a conscientious, law-abiding person. He was careful to pay his taxes. If he found an error in the bill from the feed mill he would report it, even if it were in his favor. And now he was in jail.

It was 1950, and in Pennsylvania, as well as in the rest of North America, the answer to everything was Education. The space race was just beginning, and everyone—well, almost—was enthralled by the promise and the accomplishment of modern science. Book-learning was the key to advancement, to progress, to a brighter tomorrow. The colleges were increasing their enrollment every year. Parents who had worked all their lives to eke out an existence were determined to see their children "do better."

The spirit of the times and that capital E on Education had landed Amos Beiler in jail. A devoted member of the Old Order Amish church, he had refused to send his son to school beyond Grade 8; but Pennsylvania's compulsory education law included high school. The Amish church has traditionally shunned formal education beyond Grade 8 and Amos Beiler was caught between the laws of the state and the teachings of his church. He chose to obey the church, and found himself under arrest.

"I want my son to be able to read and write and figure sums," Amos Beiler said. "Once he has that basic foundation, further head-learning is not as important as learning to apply in real life what he has learned. I want my son to learn to work. I want him to know how to care for the cows, to feed pigs, to plant corn. I want him to be able to make his own way. He will learn more that is truly useful at home than at school."

But the spirit of the times said, "Your son is being cheated. You are depriving him of his chance of advancement in the world. What if he wants to be a doctor or a lawyer?"

Amos said a doctor is all right, or a lawyer, in his place. But not everyone could be a doctor. Someone had to grow the food, or the doctors and lawyers would starve. But his logic fell on deaf ears. In 1950, it did not seem that the country could ever have too much education, too many doctors or too many lawyers.

There is a German proverb that says, *Zeit gibt Rat*. It means, "The passage of time produces counsel." This saying has certainly proven true. The passage of 30 years has vindicated Amos Beiler many times over. His ideas no longer seem so ridiculous. The pendulum has swung its full arc and, mercifully, is starting back.

One evening, ten years ago, a real-estate agent and his twelve-year-old daughter visited our farm. The agent wanted to impress upon his daughter how differently we Amish live from the rest of society. "Shirley," he said. "these people don't have any electricity."

"Oh," she said, bored.

"So they don't have any of the things we plug into the wall," Father continued, determined to make his point. "They don't have radios, or TV, or vacuum cleaners or deep freezes. They don't have dishwashers or clothes driers, or fans or toasters. They don't . . ."

Shirley's face showed interest at last.

". . .They don't go to movies or dances. They don't drive cars or put carpets on the floors. How would you like to live like that, Shirley?"

Shirley was a blunt child. "Ugh," she said. "It sounds like a prison."

Although many people today take a more benign view of our lifestyle than Shirley did, they still have many unanswered questions as to why we choose to live as we do.

Historically, the Old Order Amish are the most conservative segment of the Mennonite church. The word Amish comes from Jacob Ammann, the name of an influential leader of the late 1600s. We are direct descendants of the Anabaptists, a group that emerged from the Reformation in Switzerland around 1525. The Anabaptists felt that Zwingli, Luther, and other reformers compromised their stand, and did not go all the way in bringing the church back to a Scriptural foundation. The Anabaptists also differed from the popular reformers in that they rejected infant baptism, and insisted that the church be a voluntary brotherhood of adult believers. They were the first to advocate the separation of church and state, an idea otherwise unheard of in those days. For several centuries, the Anabaptists were persecuted relentlessly by both Protestant and Catholic authorities. Steadfastly nonviolent, they were led like sheep to their martyrdom.

Driven from their homes in Switzerland, Germany, and Alsace-Lorraine, hundreds of Amish emigrated to North America during the 150 years after 1720. Today there are Amish congregations in twenty states and one province. There are no really accurate figures, but the Amish number roughly 37,000 baptized members (baptism occurs around 18 years of age) in about 526 church districts. The three largest settlements of Amish are in Central Ohio, Lancaster County, Pennsylvania, and northern Indiana.

We are accustomed to being asked by strangers, "What have you got against electricity?" Or, "Why don't you drive cars?" Or, "Why do you dress so differently from everyone else. You know, the beards and the bonnets, and all that stuff?"

There is no simple answer to any of these questions. They

are the trees, but not the forest. One must look at our goals and way of life in order to find the answers.

For example, we feel strongly that the Bible teaches a distinct separation between the church and the world. We believe it is impossible for our church to maintain its beliefs and values if we associate freely with people who hold different values, or none at all. This is why we have not always accepted all the cultural changes that have been introduced as progress.

We are still driving horses and buggies, not because we think automobiles are wicked, but because we believe the way of life the automobile brings is breaking down the family unit and the basic structure of the community. We dress as we have for centuries because we do not care to be changing styles designed for more glamor and less modesty.

It used to be that non-Amish people would ask me, "Why is your hair so long?" During the seventies the question was, "Why is your hair so short?" My hair hadn't changed. What made it short one time and long the next?

We have chosen to live without electricity in our homes, because we feel that electricity made possible a luxurious standard of North American living unknown to previous generations. We question whether such a level of luxury is fitting to Christian people, who are to be as pilgrims on earth, travelling in search of a better world.

We live in a complex world, in which even living a simple life can be complicated. Few things come in black or white any more, but are confusing gray. There is seldom a clear line between right and wrong. It is the same with accepting change. We do accept some changes. Others we reject. Why?

We try to find out how new ideas, inventions or trends will affect us as people, as a community, as a church. If they will affect us adversely, we are wary. Many things are not what they appear to be at first glance. It is not the individual links that concern us, but the total chain. Often one thing leads to another.

In 1977, the Ontario Milk Marketing Board had a real hassle with us in Ontario. The Amish refused to accept electric-powered bulk tanks to cool our milk. The Milk Board refused to accept milk cooled in any other way. We must have appeared unreasonable to them, but it was the chain reaction we were concerned about.

Electricity to power one piece of equipment on the farm would almost certainly lead to accepting other motorized implements. Modern equipment would lead us to operate on a bigger scale. We would need more land to pay for all the bigger machinery. We would likely need a more efficient way of getting to town than the horse and buggy.

We would need our neighbors less, for, with a combine, we could forget about exchanging help at threshing time. With a forage harvester, we could fill the silo alone. With a baler, we could make our hay alone. The community would suffer. Even the family would suffer. One man could do the work of four, so father would not need his boys on the farm any more. Off they would go to work in town, exposed to influences that conflict with those of home, community, and church.

Suddenly, too late, we would wake up to discover we had crossed the thin line, and had become part of America's great melting pot. Some people might consider that prospect no great threat; but it does not happen to be what we want.

When it comes to rejecting cultural changes and inventions—somewhere in that area between black and white—we need to draw a line. It may seem like stubbornness and unreasonableness; the line may not seem to be worth drawing. But only by drawing it can we live the way we believe is right for us.

Part One:

On the Land

1 Free as the Wind

One of the first things a person notices when driving through an Amish community is that nearly every farmhouse has an old-fashioned windmill quietly pumping water. Those windmills are not there because they look quaint; they are there because they are the most practical, common-sense solution to our water-pumping needs. For years of cheap, trouble-free service, a windmill is hard to beat.

Our windmill pumps water from a 300-foot-deep well. It supplies water for our dairy herd of 16 cows, around 50 veal calves, 7 horses, and other livestock. It also pumps water for our house and for two neighboring households.

Over the last few years windmills have become popular among non-Amish people. They are being used to pump water for farms, ranches, and trout farms, and to keep ponds from drying up during the summer.

We decided to sell Baker windmills for several reasons. The only reasonable alternative for price and quality of construction is Aeromotor mills; but Bakers are perhaps slightly sturdier, and the company is free from internal and legal problems.

The construction of the Baker windmill is extremely simple. All the parts run in oil, and there is no mechanism above the oil bath, a problem spot in many other models. All bearings are cored and die cast to insure perfect castings. They are also drilled and reamed to make them absolutely smooth.

The oversize Baker wheel has 25 per cent more wind surface than the average wheel. The numerous wheel blades make for an even and steady-running mill, and collect the maximum power from light breezes. The wheel is practically storm proof; it turns itself out of the wind automatically when a certain wind force is reached.

Windmill heads are manufactured in four different sizes. Most Amish farms use the 8′ wheel, and some get by with a 6′ quite satisfactorily. Very few use the 10′ or 12′ sizes.

Some people want a windmill in front of their house or barn or shop simply for the old-fashioned look it gives to the place. If that is what you want, a 6′ wheel and short tower of 15′ or 20′ is appropriate.

However, if you really want to use the windmill, you will

get best results from a tower that puts the head 8' or 10' above all surrounding houses, barns, and trees within a 300' radius. Price of an 8' windmill is around $1,000. A 35' tower to put it on will run about that, too.

Windmill Force Pump, Model 50A
This extra-heavy force pump for deep well pump use has an oversized reservoir. Rod connection $\frac{3}{8}$" pipe to $\frac{3}{8}$" rod. Equipped with $\frac{3}{4}$" polished steel rod and brass stuffing box nut. Stroke is adjustable to 9". Compression cock spout with all-brass screw and brass cap. Flanged, adjustable-position pump head. Other pumps are also available for special installation needs. Ask us for details.
Price: around $250

Pumping Capacities of Back-Geared "Baker" Windmills
(in 15-mile-per-hour wind)

Total Elevation in Feet	6 FOOT BAKER		8 FOOT BAKER		10 FOOT BAKER		12 FOOT BAKER	
	Diameter of Cylinder Inches	U.S. Gallons Per Hour	Diameter of Cylinder Inches	U.S. Gallons Per Hour	Diameter of Cylinder Inches	U.S. Gallons Per Hour	Diameter of Cylinder Inches	U.S. Gallons Per Hour
25	3	350	3½	900	4	1250	6	2400
35	2½	240	3	720	3½	925	5	1625
50	2¼	200	2½	450	3	700	4½	1425
75	2	160	2¼	350	2½	475	4	1125
100	2	150	2	250	2½	460	3	600
125	1⅝	120	1⅞	240	2	280	2½	525
150	....	....	1¾	220	2	280	2½	525
200	....	....	....	....	1⅞	260	2	325
250	....	....	....	....	1¾	215	2	325
300	....	....	....	....	....	....	1¾	200

The above capacities are approximate. By the total elevation we do not mean the depth of the well, but the distance to the cylinder. Do not use pipe smaller than that for which the cylinders are fitted. While we recommend the above table, larger cylinders may be used with satisfaction in many circumstances.

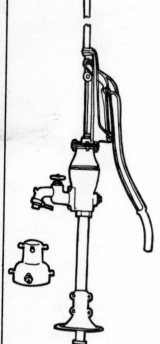

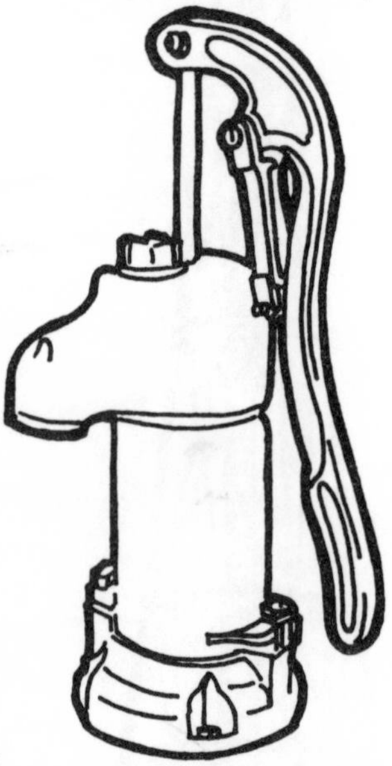

Iron Pitcher Pump
This neat, attractive pitcher pump is made of highest-grade gray iron castings. The cylinder is machined smooth and polished. Closed spout and base promote sanitation. Good-grade leather used. Modern, advanced design. Raise the handle to full height to drain cylinder and prevent freezing. Tapped for 1¼" suction pipe.
Price: around $50

Brass-lined Cylinders, Model a/40
Here is a sturdy cylinder for use with windmill pump model 50A (illustrated). Iron body, brass lined with heavy brass tubing. Equipped with outside iron caps, single leather brass cage and poppet plunger, lower brass valve seat. Available only in 2½" and 3" diameter, with 12" stroke. These two sizes are suitable for most needs. However, we have other cylinders for special needs; ask us for details.
Price: around $180

Pump Jack

A run-in-oil pump jack for use with a windmill pump. Adjustable stroke from 4½" to 6". Gear ratio 6:1. V-belt drive is quiet and efficient, eliminating all stretch and slippage.
Price: around $250

2 | Horse Power

It was September 1969 and two young Amish men were desperately trying to soothe twelve nervous draft horses that had been loaded in the belly of a chartered cargo plane.

We were on our way to a recently founded Amish settlement in Honduras, and we were worried about how well our charges were coping with the strain and stress of twentieth-century travel. We had moved the horses from Ontario to Miami by tractor-trailer, and then by plane to Honduras. Now, after five days and four thousand miles, we were relieved to be near the end of our journey, coming down at Tegucigalpa, the mountainous capital of Honduras. The horses had borne up remarkably well; their nerves seemed much less frayed than those of their human attendants.

But upon landing at the airport, we discovered to our disappointment that not enough trucks were waiting to take the horses on the last sixty miles to the fledgling Amish community. My father had tried to explain that Honduras horses are only slightly bigger than our ponies, but the truckers refused to bring more than one stock truck for twelve horses. They could not believe that they could not get twelve horses onto one truck. And so Father could only wait until the horses arrived to prove his point.

"Elephants!" the truckers cried, and a messenger was immediately dispatched to summon a second truck.

We were soon to learn that Hondurans have a second misconception about horses.

"What do you want with such big horses?" they asked.

"We want them to work the soil," the settlers explained. "We don't have tractors–just horses. We will plow with them, and till the soil for growing crops."

The natives were incredulous. "You expect them to pull?" they exclaimed. "Horses are for riding. Oxen are for pulling."

But the horses were put to work, and pull they did. They pulled so well that in only a few years, the new Amish community was known all over Honduras for its bounteous crops of garden produce, sold fresh on the streets of Tegucigalpa. Soon, not only the locals were sold on horse power; so were the top officials at the Honduras agriculture training school. They came out to the Amish community with a unique confession.

"For years we have been using the wrong approach," they said. "We have taken people from rural areas, and taught them modern methods of farming at our agricultural school, where they learn to use tractors and big machinery. But, when our students return home they do not have modern tractors and tillage equipment, and have no money to buy them. Everything they learned was wasted.

"Even if they had the equipment, it would be of little use. They rarely have large tracts of land to farm. Most were fortunate if they owned a few acres. We would have been wiser to promote small-scale farming. Even a small native horse hitched to a narrow plow would be better than planting corn with the crude wooden stick that many of them use. Please come and show us how to teach others to use horses."

It is not only the natives of Honduras who need to be taught that horses can pull—North Americans need to be reminded, too. Our land is filled with riding horses and show horses and racing horses—every kind but work horses. Most people have forgotten that horses can work.

The tools needed for a small-scale horse-operated farm are hard to find, yet every country town has two or three large mechanized-farm-implement dealers.

Yet horses are most practical for small-scale farming. They can be used almost anywhere to advantage: two horses can plow an acre each in a day and prepare the seed bed with minimum soil compaction. They step expertly between the growing rows when cultivation time comes, and haul home the harvest at the farmer's command. They won't get stuck in a wet spot, and they start easily on cold mornings. They function in snow drifts and mud, on rocks and hillsides. They can cross creeks and can be used in the woods or open fields. If a part breaks, it will usually heal itself.

Best of all, horses reproduce themselves. A mare can replace herself half a dozen times or more. (Imagine what a stir there would be over a tractor if it could give birth to a baby tractor that would take over when mother tractor got too old to work!) And fuel? Horses run on renewable energy— a small quantity of the crops they help to grow and fertilize.

Agri-Business and Efficiency

The great exodus from the land, the unsettling of America, began in our grandfathers' day. Rural populations declined over the past decades, as more and more young people abandoned the land for an urban environment. As a result, much good farm land grew only sprouts and weeds and thorns. Once-proud buildings showed signs of neglect. Rural areas suffered from too few people while urban slums and ghettoes wrestled with overcrowding, crime, and unemployment. This was "progress."

So was America's love of bigness, technology, and machines. Science was a god; education, progress, and scientific advancement, the guardians of our perfected future.

Anything as plodding, slow, and old fashioned as a horse had no place in the glorious vision.

Slowly at first, but with increasing tempo, people were coming to an uneasy awareness that something has not only gone wrong, but has been wrong all along. More people have letters after their names, but fewer are willing to dig in and work hard, to contribute to society. People did not become wiser, just more learned. Crime increased; social security systems threatened to unravel; inflation survived both the knowledgeable experts and the governments.

The Big got bigger and the Small got smaller. Companies grew while fewer farmers produced our food, and food cartels began to take on the strangulating powers of oil cartels. Our lakes are polluted and stinking; poisons are measurable even in mother's milk. The very rains that fall are retarding crop yields and killing fish. The future, which fifty years ago beckoned with such promise and hope, has arrived and left us stupefied with fear. No wonder that people who are dissatisfied with the present, and convinced the future only offers more of the same, are turning to the past. Out of the past and into the present, steps the humble horse. Is the joke of the past destined to become the hero of the future?

The Arabs, unpopular with almost everyone today, are rapidly becoming the horse's best friend. After being pushed nearly to extinction by the introduction of mass-produced tractors fifty years ago, the horse is making a heroic comeback. The struggle between tractor power and horse power is like the race between the tortoise and the hare: the steady, plodding horse is going strong, while stalled tractors search for fuel.

A Practical Alternative

We do all our field work with horses. We farm eighty acres, growing feed for our dairy herd. We plow the soil in the fall with six horses and a two-bottom plow. In the spring, we cut up the soil with a disk, and level and work it with a spring-tooth harrow. We use a drill to sow anywhere from 12 to 20 acres of oats, which we cut at harvest time with a grain binder and three horses. The binder cuts the stalks of oats, and ties them into sheaves. Eight to ten sheaves are set upright into "shocks" to dry until threshing time. Then the shocks are loaded onto wagons, taken to the barn, and put through the threshing machine, which blows the straw into the barn, and oats into the granary. Our threshing ring consists of more than a half dozen neighbors who work together threshing the grain from farm to farm.

We also plant 12 to 15 acres of corn, with which to fill our two silos. The corn is cut with a corn binder pulled by three horses. It is hauled to the silos on wagons and hand-fed into an ensilage chopper. (The chopper and threshing machine are both powered by an old tractor, kept around to provide belt-power only.) Our horses are also used for many other jobs, from cutting, raking, and loading hay to hauling manure.

Of course, horse power does not stop at the field. We use horses on the road, too. Aylmer is our main shopping center, a little more than six miles from our farm. It takes from half to three-quarters of an hour to drive each way. We usually go to town about once a week, and expect it to take a good half-day, by the time we drive in, do our business, and drive back.

Our nearest hospital is in Tillsonburg, a distance of about 12 miles. This is where our family doctor is, and we figure on about an hour and a half to drive one way. Even that does not seem long, as we rarely drive it alone. Since we do not go frequently, we actually look forward to the relaxed drive, and unhurried conversation. The only interruptions are an occasional motorist, impatiently honking his horn to get by. He has slipped up behind us without being noticed, and our horse has wandered too far to the middle of the road.

We pull quickly off to the side to let him pass. It would be a shame to delay him. Anyone who is in that much of a hurry must have a long, long way to go.

Amish Open Buggy
This is a sensible vehicle. It is the same type as those built fifty years ago, but it has such modern improvements as Timken bearings, and a stronger fifth wheel. Available with steel or rubber tires. Comes complete with shafts. All heavy-duty material and quality construction.
Price range: $1200-$1500

Wheels
We can sell buggy wheels on their own, either by the pair or in sets of four. Please specify what size wheels you need and what type of hubs you want to fit your spindles.
Price range: set of four, $500 to $600

Amish Surrey

This surrey has proven its worth over many years, taking the whole family to church or to town, or over to the neighbors for a visit. Available with or without fringed top. Steel or hard-rubber tires. With shaft for one horse or with pole for two horses.
Price: $1500 and up.

Two-seater Carriage

Here is a one-horse, two-seater carriage that can easily be converted to a hack by removing one or both of the seats. Well built and sturdy; available with either steel or hard-rubber tires. Comes complete with heavy-duty shafts of quality bent hickory.
Price: $1500 and up.

Please note: We have pictured the standard buggies and carriages most used by the Amish today. However, if you need something else, such as a Victoria, contact us for a quotation. Our buggy-maker can also do restoration work on older vehicles. Write us for details.

Harness Department

Single breast harness needs no collar

Single Pony Harness

A good-quality single harness for ponies, for use with a shaft. Complete with bridle, reins, breast, and back piece.
>*Price range: Leather—$200-$225*
>*Nylon—$125-$150*

Single Buggy Harness

A good-quality harness for pulling a buggy. Complete with bridle, reins, and breast. Does not require a collar. For average-size standard-bred horse, but can be adjusted larger or smaller within reason.
>*Price range: Leather—$275-$300*
>*Nylon—$200-$225*

Double Pony Harness

Set of double harnesses for a team of ponies, for use with a pole. Complete with bridles and reins. Includes everything you need except the collars.
>*Price range: Leather—$500-$525*
>*Nylon—$275-$300*

Double Buggy Harness

A set of double harnesses for use with a team of light horses hitched to a pole. Comes with bridle and reins. Everything you need except the collars.
>*Price range: Leather—$500-$550*
>*Nylon—$375-$425*

Double harness needing collars

Farm Team Harness

Set of good harnesses for use around the farm with a team of draft horses. This is a breeching harness, which is ideal for backing as well as pulling. Complete with bridles and reins. Collars not included.
>*Price range: Leather—$675-$750*
>*Nylon—$475-$550*

Try Our Nylon Harnesses!

The price of leather has been going up so rapidly that we have contracted a harness-maker to supply us with nylon harnesses. He uses the same type of nylon that has been used in horse halters with great success all over North America. Amish shops in the U.S. have been making these all-nylon harnesses for a number of years now, and they are rapidly gaining in popularity.

One advantage of nylon is lower costs; but there are others. Nylon is proving to be stronger than leather. It never needs oiling, does not become stiff in winter or brittle with age. It is extremely light and easy to handle—no small matter as you will know if you have ever tried to harness a team of draft horses with a heavy leather harness. If your nylon harness becomes dirty, you can simply throw it into the washing machine!

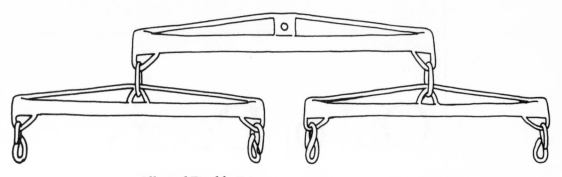

All-steel Double-tree

Designed by an Amish blacksmith and farm-tested for many years, this all-steel welded double-tree is lightweight enough for easy handling, yet heavy-duty enough to withstand great strain. Reinforced at the spots where wear normally occurs, for extra-long life. Invest in a double-tree you can depend on.
Price: under $50

Shafts

These are the shafts we sell with all our buggies and carriages. They are heavy duty, and have proved very sturdy. We have had horses throw themselves while in harness, and get back up; but they have never even cracked these shafts. Sold in kit form only. You do the assembling and painting, but no special tools are needed.
Price: $50

Collars

Pony Collars

A good collar is a must for pulling a heavy load. These collars come in sizes 13", 14", 15", and 16".
Price range: $50 and up

Buggy Collars

These come in a range of sizes: 15", 16", 17", and 18".
Price range: $70 and up.

Collars for Draft Horses

These are the Canadian Work Collar No. 49, and come in sizes 19", 20", 21", 22", and 23". Larger sizes are also available at extra cost. We can also get a variety of other collars for you on request.
Price range; $80 and up.

Bickmore's Gall Salve

This old-fashioned gall salve is every bit as good as the manufacturer claims it is. At our farm, we would not want to try to get along without Bickmore's. In the spring, when field work starts, the horses are soft and almost certain to develop sores under the collar or where the harness rubs. Applied consistently, Bickmore's will heal almost miraculously, even if the horse continues at work. If horses could vote, it would likely soon be illegal not to have a jar of Bickmore's in the medicine cabinet. As far as we are concerned, there is nothing like it. And it is unbelievably inexpensive.
A year's supply for one horse costs under $5.

3 | Out of Doors

—by Jo Ann Gardner

A Tale of Self-Reliance

We had our first garden almost twenty-five years ago. It was small, but produced an abundance of food for our growing family of four children. Since we didn't own a freezer, we learned how to can all our surplus vegetables. Used jars were inexpensive and easy to find, since most people who used to can foods were buying freezers and were glad to be rid of their canning jars. We collected hundreds in this way.

Over the years our garden grew, and we never needed to buy vegetables at any time of the year. We moved to more remote rural areas and began to keep chickens, which supplied us with all the eggs we needed. We learned to make soap and to gather and dry edible mushrooms. Since we rented farms, we were never able to establish many fruit crops; but we gathered great quantities of apples from abandoned orchards for applesauce and cider and vinegar. We picked wild strawberries, chokecherries, wild grapes, mountain cranberries, blueberries, and sometimes rhubarb from around an old cellar hole. We made jam, juice, and preserves from the fruit. We learned to hunt and prepare wild game. Ducks, geese, rabbits, raccoons, squirrels, pigeons, quails, woodchucks, and venison gave us a varied, healthy diet.

On our first rented farm we had a cow, a pig, a borrowed horse, some laying hens, and broiler chickens. We learned how to make butter, render lard, make pork sausage, and cure and smoke our hams and bacon. We also learned how to use cross-cut saws and axes to cut the winter's wood.

Through this experience, which lasted for two years, we came to understand the discipline and work that is necessary to become self-reliant. Since we had little money, no vehicle, and lived five miles from the nearest town, we constantly had to "make-do" with the materials at hand—or do without. We made our toothpowder from baking soda and a dash of salt. Worn-out boot socks were turned into dolls; little boats and trucks were made from scraps of wood.

Horse-drawn farm equipment, which we found or bought for very little money, was often worn out and rusty. We learned to repair it, fashioning parts from the materials at hand. Children's shirts were made out of skirts or dresses; snowpants and jackets could be made from larger pants and old coats.

Gradually our farming operation grew, and we developed the skills to make cheese. Once we had our own farm, we were able to supply all our food needs except for basic items such as flour, sugar, salt, and tea. We raised many more pigs and learned to make and preserve more pork products such as liverwurst and scrapple. We slaughtered our old laying hens and turned them into soup, which we canned. We raised our own beef and chickens as well, canning and processing them ourselves. Since we lived near the water, we learned all about fish-processing and were able to clean and brine, smoke and can as much as 300 pounds of herring at a time.

We raised large quantities of whatever fruit was suitable for a northeastern maritime climate: strawberries, raspberries, gooseberries, currants, plums, pears, apples, rhubarb, and blueberries. We processed them all in various ways, so that we enjoy fruit year round without buying any from a store.

We also built an ice-house and learned to cut and store ice, so we could enjoy fresh ice cream in the summer. We have learned, too, to raise the herbs we need for flavoring and medicine: dill for pickles, coriander for sausage, sage for pork and cheese, wormwood for moth flakes, horehound for sore throats. Herbs also support our bees, which supply us with honey for baking.

We enjoy the products of our labor. Such quality could not be bought at any price, and we also enjoy the challenge of providing for many of our needs ourselves; but we are by no means self-sufficient.

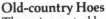

Garden Cultivator

Two wheels support the cultivating tools on this Earthway garden cultivator. It has a convenient depth-adjustment feature, and comes complete with three attachments: a five-tine cultivator, a slicing hoe, and a furrow plow. Takes the drudgery out of manual cultivating. One-year guarantee from date of purchase on factory-installed parts and workmanship.
Price: under $70

Old-country Hoes

These imported hoes have the heft and feel of the old-fashioned quality tools they are. They are pictured here without handles; but rest assured, they do come with handles that are easy to install.
Price range: $8-$10 each

The Bell Corn Sheller

This corn sheller is designed for dry ear corn or walnuts. It is easily operated by a hand crank. Made of first-quality cast iron, it is painted with a rich non-toxic red finish. It attaches to barrel or box by means of clamps that are an integral part of each unit. Shells easily and cleanly, depositing corn in box or barrel to which it is fastened. Cob ejector and tipping attachment included. Spring adjusts to fit all size ears. Capacity 10 to 15 bushels per hour. Has 8¼" picker wheel. Weight 20 lbs.
Price: $70

Garden Seeder

Built by Earthway, this garden seeder is a great time-saver, especially if you have a large garden. Six seed plates provide for accurate spacing, whether you are planting corn, beans, peas, radishes, carrots, beets, or whatever. It digs the trench, drops in the seed and covers it up. All you do is simply push the seeder along the row. It comes equipped with a marker, which automatically marks off the next row at the correct distance. To obtain satisfactory results with this seeder, it is important that the soil be free of hard chunks of earth and poorly tilled spots. One-year guarantee from date of purchase on factory-installed parts and workmanship.
Price: under $70

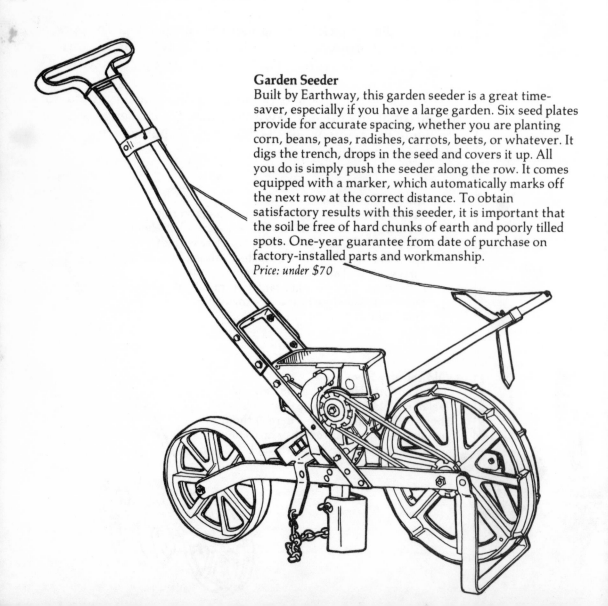

Martins, Mice and Mosquitoes

4

—by Joseph Stoll

The Purple Martin, Our Most Wanted Bird

Among birds, there is nothing quite like the purple martin. When God created the feathered species, I like to think he designed the purple martin as a special gift to man. Graceful and swift of flight, this largest of the swallow family is friendly and sociable around humans. He is a first-rate singer, and never eats cherries or scratches in the garden. He has clean habits, and will not mess up the lawn.

As if a pleasant personality were not enough, the purple martin is a splendid insect exterminator, normally matching his own weight each day in captured bugs. A single bird can eat 2000 mosquitoes a day. Multiply this by the number of birds in a colony and the number of days in a summer, and you will see why the purple martin is recognized as a means of insect control.

Many people in North America are not familiar with the purple martin, even though over the past twenty years this bird has managed to catch the public eye again and again, and has gained thousands of new friends. The purple martin is the only bird with a thriving newspaper devoted to it, *The Purple Martin News.* (Since June, 1979 the name has been changed to *Nature Society News.*) Each spring, throughout the land, new martin houses are being erected on lawns and in gardens. Then the aspiring landlords wait expectantly for their tenants to return from the winter holiday in Brazil.

Let me assure you there are substantial reasons for the purple martin's popularity.

The purple martin *(Progne subis)* is by far the best singer among the swallows; its only close rival is its smaller cousin, the barn swallow. The martin's song has been variously described as "a liquid, rolling twitter" and "a bubbling chatter." Once heard, it is not easily forgotten.

The male and female birds are similar in appearance until the second year, when the male takes on a shiny blue-black coloring, hence the name, *purple* martin. His average length is about 8" and his weight perhaps 4 oz. The female is slightly smaller, and has a duller and less uniform color, with pale gray breast and abdomen. The immature males are similar in appearance to the females, and are easily confused with them. (After their first summer with a martin house, one young couple in our county complained because all they could get was "two pairs of grayish swallows." Next year they hoped to have martins!)

Purple martins spend their winter vacation in Brazil, mainly in the Amazon Valley jungles, but they do not nest there. The first birds to return in the spring are the "scouts," usually mature males. These may show up as early as January in the southern United States, but are not likely to be seen in Ontario before the first of April. The main body of migrants will arrive several weeks later. Actual nesting begins in mid-May or early June in most parts of Canada.

As a rule, the birds that nest in your house one year and many of the young you raise, will return to the same site in years to follow. This means that once you have a colony established, you can be reasonably sure of martins each year. I have seen it happen that a wooden house was taken down for the winter, and the landlord was tardy in setting it up again in the spring. The martins returned to the exact site where their house had stood the previous year, and flew about, scolding and chattering.

What is the summer nesting range of the purple martin? The areas of heaviest concentration seem to be central and southern parts of the United States, and up into Ontario and Quebec, as far north as Montreal. There are fewer martins in the New England states and the Maritime provinces, but they are there, too. Farther west, the ranks also thin out as the land becomes drier, and has correspondingly fewer insects and a sparse human population.

Surprisingly enough, the range extends well to the north in the prairie provinces; large numbers are found in the Edmonton region and as far north as Great Slave Lake. West of the Rockies, along the coastal area, the purple martin is replaced by its nearly identical cousin, the western martin, which also nests in man-made houses.

Only in the northern parts of Canada and in the Rocky Mountain regions of the United States is the bird entirely absent.

I grew up with purple martins. Nearly all Amish farms have martin houses, and ours was no exception. As a young lad, I could no more imagine a summer without martins, than I could picture a winter without snow. Some of my fondest memories are of waking up on a sunny spring morning to martin music outside our farmhouse window–the melodious warbling of several dozen birds, who would pause occasionally to twitter and gossip.

In those days we were not yet aware how great were the benefits of our martin colony in the control of troublesome insects. We knew they fed entirely on the wing, but we didn't bother to count the mosquitoes before and after. We put up martin houses each spring because we enjoyed them and their music.

Martins are social birds, who like to live in colonies.

Originally, they nested in the forest in hollow trees, or in abandoned woodpecker holes. Today they nest almost entirely in man-made houses, and adapt readily to either country living or a suburban backyard. They even have been known to nest in traffic lights above noisy city streets.

The Indians were the first to lure the martin to prearranged housing. They carved entry holes in gourds, and hung them up near their teepees. When the white settlers came, they followed the example of the Indians, and either hung up gourds or built crude wooden houses for the friendly birds.

The martins thrived until the Europeans made the horrible mistake of introducing the starling and the house sparrow to North America. The starlings and sparrows spread across the countryside, agressively confiscating every available tree hole and bird house for their own use. The martins were no match; the finely tuned balance of nature had been upset. After about 1900, the purple martin population went into decline.

A second crippling blow hit the purple martins when they began to die of the effects of chemical pesticides widely and carelessly used.

In recent years, however, the growing interest in the purple martin and a major breakthrough in martin-house designing have helped the bird begin a determined comeback. The use of lightweight aluminum houses that can be easily raised and lowered has eliminated the starling as a threat to nesting martins and has made the control of sparrows easier and more successful.

The purple martin may yet have the last word in its battle against pesticides. Martins have become popular at many parks and resorts as an alternative to chemical insect control. A number of towns and cities in the United States no longer use insecticides on their parks areas. They have set up martin houses instead, with a proven record of success. A notable example is the city of Griggsville, Illinois.

Although the martin feeds exclusively on flying insects–gnats, flies, mosquitoes, whatever is available–it does not disturb the honey bee. Many purple martin colonies exist side by side with colonies of bees, and all is peaceful.

Purple martins are clean birds. Last summer I relaxed on the lawn with several of my sons after a long day in the hayfield. We were intrigued by the martins feeding their young. A mother bird came swooping down and braked to a stop, a large gnat in her bill. The youngster whose turn it was for supper stretched his head out of the doorway, mouth gaping. With a gulp the gnat was gone.

After such a meal, nature has its way. The youngster quickly changed position, and shoved his opposite end out the door. The faithful mother was waiting. She caught the waste sac in her beak and was off, skimming high above the field to drop it far away.

Becoming a landlord to purple martins may require patience. Not everyone who puts up a house in the spring can expect to have martins nesting that summer, although the odds are good. (Incidentally, the addition of a second or third house seems to increase the probability of getting started successfully.)

The best place to set up your martin house is in an open area of lawn or garden, at least 20' away from trees or buildings. Perhaps the martins like the open space in which to fly, but they also have an instinctive fear of predators such as cats and snakes that might be lurking in the trees.

You may find that martins will make an inspection tour of your house, then leave again without signing any papers. Do not be discouraged. Birds have preferences, just as humans do, when they go house-shopping. Perhaps the next martin that comes along will decide your house is just what he was looking for.

A body of water such as a pond, lake or river will increase your chances, as the martins apparently feed on the insects flying above the water. Yet a pond or a river nearby is not essential. Many large colonies are situated far from a body of water.

Another bonus that martins appreciate is a place to perch. They spend their idle moments along a telephone line or electric wire. We generally stretch up a wire especially for our martins. Auxiliary perches can also be bought to go with the aluminum houses.

When is the best date to set up your martin house? There is a slight advantage in getting it up early, as soon as scouts reach your area. But this advantage can be offset by the fact that you are giving the sparrows and starlings a head start. Keep in mind that most new colonies in Canada do not receive their first permanent tenants till mid-May or later, and often not till June.

Perhaps the greatest deterrent to successful martin-keeping has been the competition from the starling and the house sparrow. Even as a lad, I knew that everyone who puts up a martin house will have birds nesting in that house. It is up to the landlord to decide which tenants he wants. If he wants purple martins, he will have to control the starlings and sparrows. If he wants sparrows and starlings, well, how stupid can you get?

We grew up believing the only good starlings and sparrows were dead ones. We set up our martin houses purposely where they were within range of the BB gun and the .22, and we shot the sparrows and starlings. The martins didn't mind the shooting; at every crack of the rifle, they flew into the air and cheered. It was the only way to have purple martins.

Times have changed somewhat. With the advent of the aluminum houses, the starling has been eliminated from the competition. Starlings insist on a dark, dingy hole, and have never been known to nest in an aluminum house. They are still a nuisance in other ways, but they have ceased to be a threat to purple martins.

The plucky little sparrow has not given up so easily; but he, too, is experiencing hard times. The aluminum houses can be lowered once a week or so and the sparrow nests removed. If the sparrows are as intelligent as they ought to be, they will eventually get the message and look elsewhere for a nesting site.

Once martins are firmly established, they can pretty well hold their own against sparrows. They have no scruples about ganging up on a lone sparrow family, and even forcefully evicting them. But martins are not likely to gain such a numerical advantage without the help of humans.

I am sure the sparrow and the starling do have virtues, perhaps more than we have realized. But my sympathies are still 100 per cent with the purple martin, and I think man ought to make some atonement for having brought the sparrow and the starling across the ocean in the first place. There may be people who disagree, and claim we shouldn't be prejudiced against any bird species. I grant them the right to disagree, but I hope they won't put up any martin houses. They don't need martins anyway. Anyone who gets along with sparrows and starlings should have no problem with mosquitoes!

The Purple Martin House

Once you have decided to try to attract purple martins to your home, the next step is to obtain a suitable house. You may wish to buy an aluminum house because of their convenience and superiority. Or you may decide to build your own house of wood.

If you are reasonably handy with a hammer and saw, and like to work with wood, you will find it is not difficult to build a martin house. Here are some points to keep in mind:

Martins love close neighbors. Their houses should have multiple nesting compartments. The minimum is six compartments, which will supply nesting room for half a dozen families. A house twice as large is better. Each compartment must have an entrance hole about $2\frac{1}{4}$" in diameter, and be separated by interior partitions from the other compartments. The house may be built several storeys high. An exterior grade of $\frac{1}{2}$" plywood works fine for floors, and may also be used for the roof.

The recommended dimensions of each compartment is a 6" cube: 6" wide each way and 6" high.

A porch or veranda about 3" wide is needed in front of each entrance hole, and may extend all the way around the house. An added feature is to place guard rails along the outside of the veranda to keep the fledgling young from falling to the ground.

Each storey and the roof should be hinged or otherwise designed for dismantling, so that the house can be cleaned out easily and thoroughly each fall.

The house should be designed so it can be fastened and detached from the post, an annual event if the house is taken down for the winter. The post itself can be a 4 x 4 purchased from the lumberyard, or a straight pole cut from the bush. The house should be raised to a height of 12'-14' and the post secured so it does not blow down in a high wind.

The completed house should be painted, preferably white or some other light color to reflect heat and make a cooler home.

The roof, however, is commonly painted a darker color such as green or brown. A piece of styrofoam or insulation can be placed in the "attic", just under the roof, to make the house more comfortable during the hot summer months.

The martin enthusiast who elects to buy his house should be grateful to the Trio Manufacturing Company of Griggsville, Illinois, who in the early 1960s pioneered the development of the aluminum martin house. Other manufacturers have followed their example, so that, today, American buyers have a variety to select from. Even Sears is selling them by mail order from Chicago. However, the Trio company remains the world's largest builder of purple martin houses.

Now, I must confess that I was brought up with the tradition (strengthened in my mother's kitchen) that the homemade is invariably better than the store-bought. So when I first learned of these aluminum martin houses, I was skeptical. It sounded like a good deal for the manufacturer, and not so good for the buyer and the birds. But I have been overwhelmed by the evidence to the contrary.

The factory-built houses that I have seen in use are scientifically designed with a genuine concern for the occupants. They contain extra features that cannot be duplicated in a homemade wooden house.

The greatest single advantage in these lightweight aluminum houses is that they can be easily raised and lowered vertically, so that sparrow cleanout and nest checking can be done without harming the martin nests. These houses come complete with a steel post. The larger models such as the Trio 24-hole Castle, are fitted with a winch and cable; the smaller houses use a rope lanyard, raising and lowering the house like a flag. Even semi-invalids in wheelchairs can take care of their own purple martin colonies.

Other valuable features of the aluminum houses are these: Fewer problems with mites and other parasites; they are heat-reflecting so the house is cooler in the summer; individually hinged entrance doors ease observation and cleanout; shiny interiors discourage starlings from nesting; guard rails keep the young birds from falling to the ground; a baked paint enamel finish makes the houses virtually maintenance free; and handy winter door stops allow the house to be left up the year round.

If you hope to make building a martin house a project for your teenager, the aluminum houses still have something to offer. Most are sold in kit form with step-by-step instructions. At our house, the children quarrelled for a turn at assembling. It turned out to be fun for the whole family.

If you have never had any experience whatever with purple martins, you may want to visit an established colony near you and observe them firsthand. You may wish to read up on them or subscribe to *Nature Society News—The Purple Martin Newspaper.* (Issued monthly at Griggsville, Illinois 62340; $7.00 a year in Canada; $6.00 in U.S.A.)

Purple martins are one of man's finest allies in his efforts to control bothersome insects. They are a pleasant pastime for young and old, backyard friends worthy of your attention. Having martins as your guests provides a summer-long thrill: the first "scouts" arriving back from the south; the busy days of nest-building; the feeding of the young; and then the new generation trying out their wings in readiness for that long flight to Brazil.

Before you realize it, the martins have left for the tropics, the air is empty, the lawn is quiet. With a sinking feeling you realize your friends of the summer have deserted you. There is one consolation–on a bright day next April they will be back!

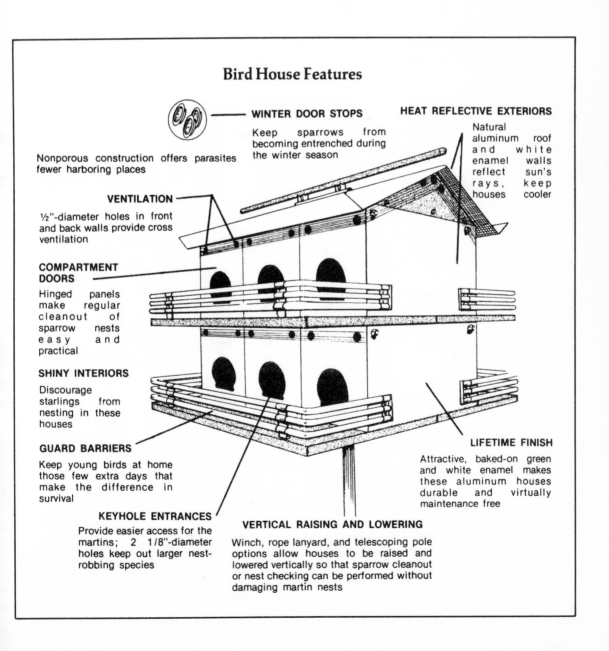

Bird House Features

WINTER DOOR STOPS

Keep sparrows from becoming entrenched during the winter season

HEAT REFLECTIVE EXTERIORS

Natural aluminum roof and white enamel walls reflect sun's rays, keep houses cooler

Nonporous construction offers parasites fewer harboring places

VENTILATION

½"-diameter holes in front and back walls provide cross ventilation

COMPARTMENT DOORS

Hinged panels make regular cleanout of sparrow nests easy and practical

SHINY INTERIORS

Discourage starlings from nesting in these houses

GUARD BARRIERS

Keep young birds at home those few extra days that make the difference in survival

KEYHOLE ENTRANCES

Provide easier access for the martins; 2 1/8"-diameter holes keep out larger nest-robbing species

LIFETIME FINISH

Attractive, baked-on green and white enamel makes these aluminum houses durable and virtually maintenance free

VERTICAL RAISING AND LOWERING

Winch, rope lanyard, and telescoping pole options allow houses to be raised and lowered vertically so that sparrow cleanout or nest checking can be performed without damaging martin nests

World's Finest Bird Houses For Our
Most Wanted Bird

12-family Trio-Wade
With crank-up pole. A deluxe house developed by J.L. Wade, the nation's foremost martin authority. Big, wrap-around porch with extra-wide guard rails gives young birds an exercise area running right around the house. Winch and cable for easy, safe raising and lowering. New dri-nest removable sub-floors. Complete with steel pole, winch assembly, and winter door stops. Easy to assemble.
21" x 24" x 16" high. Kit weight 50 lbs.

12-family Trio-Musselman
The house that pioneered Trio inventions. Attractive green and white baked enamel finish. Individual hinged compartment doors. Guard Barriers to protect babies. Keyhole entrances recommended by naturalists. Mounting bracket fits 1¼" standard pipe. Easy-to-assemble kit or factory assembled. With winter door stops.
18" x 19" x 16" high. Kit weight 13 lbs.

8-family Trio-Grandma
Meets all requirements for attracting martins. Easy care for your colony at modest price. Complete with new raising lanyard, galvanized post, and winter door stops. Guard barriers protect baby birds. Full-size cavities.
12" x 18" x 15" high. Kit weight 25 lbs.

12-family Trio-Grandpa

With rope lanyard. The easiest of
all martin systems to maintain
and use. Easy assembly.
Complete with 14' steel post,
nylon raising lanyard, and winter
door stops. Self-draining,
removable dri-nest subfloors.
18" x 20" x 16" high. Kit weight
33 lbs.

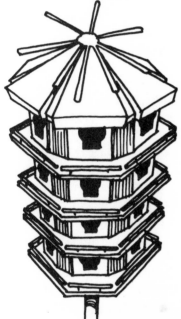

24-family Trio-Castle

With crank-up pole. Easy
assembly. Raise or lower house
with two fingers. Includes
galvanized-steel pole, winch
assembly, removable dri-nest
subfloors for drainage, and
winter door stops.
25" x 30" high. Kit weight 62 lbs.

Martin houses priced $100 and up

Accessories

Martin House Perch (MHPA)

Folded for extra strength, 3 30"
arms offer comfortable perches
for martins. Fits 1¼" diameter
pipe. Fits MPQ and MP14 posts
and TW12 systems. Weight:
2 lbs.
Price: $15-$20

Telescoping Mounting Post (MP14)

Heavy-guage galvanized-steel
three-section post telescopes
from 5' to 14'. Pipe sections 1¾",
1½" and 1¼" with sturdy steel
clamping members. For Trio-
Musselman 6 and 12 cavity
houses. Tested to withstand
strong winds. Weight: 20 lbs.
Price: $40-$50

Heavy-duty 3-Section Post (MPQ)

Has quick-lock clamps. Simply
raise locking handle to loosen
clamping members. Speedy
adjustment 5' to 14'. Fits Trio-
Musselman 6 and 12 cavity
houses. Tested to 85 mph winds.
Weight: 26 lbs.
Price: $60-$70

Mounting-post Socket (MPS and TGS)

Hot-dipped galvanized-steel pipe,
24" long. Provides firm base for
mounting post. Fits 1¾" O.D.
pipe. MPS fits MPQ and TW12.
TGS fits TG8 and TG12.
Price: $15

Sparrow Trap

This fully tested, effective trap can help rid your lawn and garden of messy English sparrows. Each unit has two traps and a storage area the birds enter themselves. The gentle action will not harm birds. Heavy-guage galvanized-wire netting with aluminum feed trays and trip perches. Will give years of service. Fully assembled, with quick removal mounting bracket for pipe up to 1¾" O.D.
24½" x 10" x 26". Weight 5¾ lbs.
Price: $30-$35

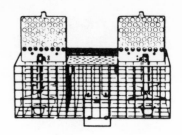

A Better Mousetrap

Sixty years ago, A.E. Kness, an Iowa high-school janitor grew tired of finding mice nibbling at his lunch. Always a practical man, he decided to do something about it: invent a better mousetrap. His shoe-box-shaped, catch-'em-alive invention has stood the test of time. Although the company (still kept in the Kness family) does no advertising and employs no salesmen on the road, the world is beating a path to its door. Ten years ago, the Kness Manufacturing Company employed only four workers, who managed a daily output of 60 traps. Today, 28 workers turn out 2,500 mousetraps a day.

There is a reason for the growing popularity of the Kness' trap. It not only catches mice alive without bait, it can capture up to fifteen in one setting. Although they do not even mention it in their literature–unlike the usual American-style sales pitch–the Knesses do stand behind their product with an absolute lifetime guarantee. Last year, a plastic company persuaded the Knesses to use a plastic wind-up key rather than a metal one; but the plastic part proved inferior. Embarrassed, the Knesses voluntarily replaced the traps that broke, and sent new ones with the traditional metal parts to all 60,000 purchasers of the potentially defective product.

We know this product works. At our farm it has proved more valuable than a dozen cats. We feel this company deserves the well-earned success it is enjoying today for marketing a practical product in a practical manner at a price that is as outdated as their way of doing business.

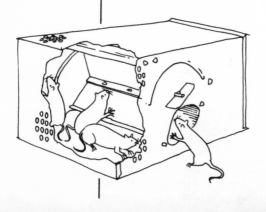

Ketch-all Mouse Trap

Set it just once to catch up to 15 mice. No bait required. When a mouse enters to explore this curious device, a hair trigger is released and the creature is harmlessly spanked into the hopper by a revolving door. The trap, which is wound up like a clock, is automatically set for the next mouse. Built of heavy-guage galvanized steel, it is built to last. Completely safe around children and pets.
Price: under $15

The Apple Orchard

5

Many old, abandoned homesteads have apple orchards. The trees were planted in an age when people expected to live at the same spot most of their lives and to reap the fruit of their labors. Today, many of these orchards are sad sights indeed—branches untrimmed, starlings nesting in rotting limbs, and the premises overgrown with weeds and burdocks. But apparently a few people are rediscovering the value of these orchards. Some are being reclaimed and cleaned up.

We get a number of letters from people who say, "We have access to an old orchard, and it is surprising how many apples those trees still bear, in spite of the years of neglect they have been subjected to. We need a cider press . . ."

The Pioneer Place Cider Press

We feel our rugged home-size press is designed to stand up to years of use, yet it is lightweight and portable, so it can be easily moved indoors or out. It is constructed of kiln-dried, pressure-treated sturdy 2" natural pine, so it works great, and looks good, too. In fact, our press is really two machines in one: a fruit press and an apple grinder.

The Press

Our pressing hopper of finished hardwood will hold a full 12 quarts. It is specially designed to give most juice from each pressing: as the diameter (10") is smaller than the hopper height (13"), no juice must be forced a long way to the outer edge; therefore less juice gets wasted, trapped in the pomace. The wood is treated with a natural oil finish guaranteed not to taint fruit or juice. Heavy galvanized-steel bands bind the hopper together.

The press stands 37" high. Its tapered-leg construction adds great stability when pressing or grinding. All the joints are dadoed and cross-bolted for extra strength. A heavy-duty ¾" acme rod gives you extra pressure to coax out that last drop of juice.

The Grinder

The fruit grinder is mounted on the side of the press so the pulped apples will drop directly into the hopper below. However, it can easily be mounted independently of the press, so both pressing and grinding can take place at the same time. Stainless-steel teeth mounted on a 4" hardwood cylinder slash whole apples (or other fruit) into a pulp for easy pressing. Special 1"-thick laminated plywood on the sides of the grinder hopper adds bearing support and overall strength.

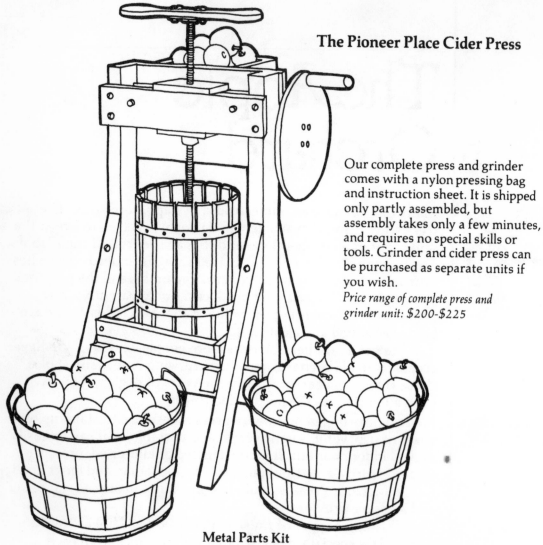

The Pioneer Place Cider Press

Our complete press and grinder comes with a nylon pressing bag and instruction sheet. It is shipped only partly assembled, but assembly takes only a few minutes, and requires no special skills or tools. Grinder and cider press can be purchased as separate units if you wish.

Price range of complete press and grinder unit: $200-$225

Metal Parts Kit

Here is a kit for the handyman who would like to make his own press, but needs the metal parts: acme rod, grinder teeth, bolts, nuts, and screws. Our kit includes all the metal parts for both grinder and press, the 4" hardwood cylinder for the grinder, and the wooden handle for the grinder wheel. All the other wooden parts can be purchased at your local lumber yard. Comes with instruction sheet.

Price range: $85-$100

White Mountain Apple Parer

This old-fashioned machine looks so simple that a person is tempted to think the advertisements are joking when they claim, "It peels, cores, and slices your apples in one operation." But it really does exactly that, provided the apples are comparatively fresh. If they have been kept in storage until the peelings become a bit leathery, this parer does not work too well. But, if you have fresh apples, you will be pleasantly surprised by this efficient machine. Made of cast-iron and plated-steel parts for a lifetime of use.

Price: around $30

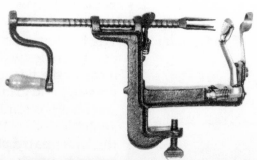

Grow Your Own Cow

6

She was everything Tom and Betty Anderson had dreamed of–young, gentle, soft brown eyes, a well-formed udder, beautifully curved horns. Bossy's stanchion was ready for her, with a supply of hay and grain, and a bit of straw for bedding. Tonight there would be fresh, rich, whole Jersey milk to put on the table, foaming with flavor, goodness, and country nutrition. Soon there would be cream for coffee, homemade butter, homemade cheese. . . . This was the moment they had been waiting for.

"Oh, I'm so glad we decided on a Jersey," Betty gushed. "Those Holsteins they had at the auction–you know, they were so big and hulking, and so commercial-looking."

Tom picked up the rustic, three-legged stool he had made, and tried to appear confident. He took the pail between his legs, and moved closer to Bossy. The last thing he remembered was wondering vaguely whether there was any special significance in the way she was rolling her eyes at him, or whether that was the way of all cows. And then, *Wham.*

Tom lay sprawling in the gutter.

As soon as Betty was certain that Tom was more damaged in his dignity than in his bones, she burst out laughing. "I'm sorry," she apologized. "But you looked so funny."

Tom failed to see the joke. He had a job to do, and he intended to see it through. He retrieved his rustic stool, and approached Bossy again. Once more, rolling eyes, flying hoofs, sprawling Tom, laughing wife.

Tom tried another approach–breaking his rustic stool squarely across Bossy's back.

In the end, the cow was so jumpy she lashed out wildly every time Tom approached her. Humbling as it was, there remained nothing to do but go to Neighbor Johnson and summon professional help. (The Johnsons milked 150 cows.)

Neighbor Johnson soon had things under control. He calmed Bossy down, and quietly milked her. He also gave Tom some tips about how to tie a rope around Bossy so she couldn't kick. (See "Kicking Problems", in pages 52-53.)

The only part of the evening that really turned out like a dream was the amount of milk the new cow gave. She came close to filling a two-gallon pail.

"She's a real good milker, at any rate," Tom announced, more to console himself than to inform his neighbor.

"She is tonight," Neighbor Johnson said dryly. "Tomorrow will be different. I would guess she hasn't been milked for two days."

The neighbor's predictions proved correct. Bossy gave less than a full quart in the morning, and the milk in one quarter of her udder was chunky. It was the Anderson's introduction to mastitis, an udder infection they were to learn a lot more about in the weeks ahead.

"I guess we got a lemon," Tom remarked.

"Well, you know," replied Johnson, "the only cows I send to the auction are my culls. A lot of other farmers do the same. The odds were against you. You might have been better off buying a heifer calf and raising your own cow."

Train Up A Calf

Although buying a calf has the disadvantage of requiring two years before you have milk for the table, there are advantages, too. The first, and perhaps most obvious one, is cost. A heifer calf may sell for only about 10 to 15 per cent of the price of her mother. I watched a week-old Jersey heifer calf auctioned in the spring of 1980 for $28. (A good Holstein heifer calf might bring $150–$200. This is much more than the Jersey, but still only a fraction of what a Holstein cow might sell for.) Not only is the first cost much lower, but the cow you grow will be cheaper in the end, too, especially if you have grazing for her in the summer.

The second advantage of buying a calf is the opportunity to train her. A lot of homesteaders lack fenced fields, and it is essential that they are able to lead their cow, and tie her for grazing. Most adult cows in Canada are not trained for leading. Any attempt to lead an untrained adult cow will almost certainly end up with her leading you. But a calf can soon be persuaded you are the boss. If you lead her regularly, she will soon follow without resistance.

Be sure to subject your calf to other handling beyond leading and tying. Touch her frequently around the legs and udder area to get her accustomed to being handled. (But do not actually "milk" on the teats, as pressure on the teat canal could permit bacteria to enter, causing mastitis problems later.)

Perhaps it isn't the calf that is being trained as much as her owner. Familiarity with your calf will not breed contempt, it will inspire confidence. It is amazing how differently a cow will treat you if you have been around her for nearly two years. Animals are quick to sense fear and panic; but they are just as quick to sense confidence, and will respond accordingly.

The third reason for growing your own cow is quality. You are not guaranteed a top milker when you raise your own calf, but you have a much better chance. At least, you are not starting in where a previous owner gave up.

**Cheaper
By The Pair**

If you are buying a heifer calf to raise as the family cow, you may wish to buy a bull calf at the same time. Here are the factors in favor of such a decision:

Very little extra time is required to care for the second calf.

You will have a bull to use for breeding purposes at 16–18 months of age, when your heifer will have reached sufficient maturity. (Bulls can be used for service any time after 12 months.)

The bull calf, besides being available to breed your heifer, will provide you with your year's beef supply, and should be slaughtered as soon as the heifer is safely in calf.

Although this may be debatable, it is my opinion that calves enjoy company, and two calves will do better than one.

You may have been told, quite rightly, that you cannot afford to keep a bull around for servicing your family cow. Besides being expensive to feed, bulls tend to become ugly tempered and dangerous as they grow older. But by starting a young bull calf every year, you overcome these problems. You are not keeping a bull just for breeding; you are raising your beef. The fact that you can use him for breeding services once he is a year old, before you slaughter him, is just an extra bonus. If you don't keep a bull after he is 16 months, you escape the worst hazards, as bulls rarely become dangerous before that age. But be warned: you must pen your heifer and bull calf separately after about six months of age, otherwise you risk your heifer becoming pregnant too young, which can keep her from ever growing to be full sized.

Where To Buy

A cattle auction is often the easiest place to pick up calves. However, there are pitfalls here, especially for someone lacking experience. Sale barns are notorious for diseases. Your calf, while under stress, is subjected to hybrid germs from dozens of farms. Also, you know nothing of the calf's history. How old is she? What problems has she had before you bought her? Why is she being sold? (She may have been sick for two weeks, and be immune to every antibiotic in the vet's black bag.)

But most important, you do not know what your calf has been given from a bag more magic than the vet's–the cow's udder, and the vital colostrum it produces for the newborn calf. It is difficult to overemphasize the importance of a calf drinking its mother's colostrum-rich milk within several hours of birth. Farmers have always known this was important, but for a long time it was not known why. Today we know that a mother's first milk is fortified with custom-made antibodies that provide an immune factor against disease.

At our farm, when a cow freshens, the first thing we do is get some of that colostrum milk down the calf's throat, the sooner the better. Under no circumstance should more than six hours be allowed to elapse, and less than two hours is best. Calves purchased at a salesbarn may well never have had a drink of colostrum. Many large dairy operations put little value on calves, especially bull calves, and simply ship them off to the nearest auction. Let the buyer beware: although your calf may look like a big, strong, husky fellow, without colostrum he stands a good chance of succumbing to some disease.

The ideal way to buy a calf is to go directly to a farmer, and tell him what you want. It may be difficult to find a heifer calf this way, as most dairy farmers keep their heifer calves for replacement cows. But you can certainly pick up any number of bull calves directly from a farmer. If the calf is less than 24 hours old, request a gallon or two of its mother's milk to take with you.

If you are unable to buy what you want directly from a farmer, and must resort to a sale barn, observe carefully the following precautions.

Avoid droopy calves. Bid only on calves that are bright eyed, alert and frisky. If a calf stands and droops its head or even its ears, let someone else buy it. Shun any calf that staggers and appears small, weak or puny. The older a calf, the lower will be the risk factor. Normally, the older and larger the calf, the more resistance she has to disease, and the better her chance of recovery should she become sick. But remember that you cannot tell the age of a calf by its size alone. Some calves at birth are twice the size of others.

Watch for signs of scours. Scours, animal diarrhea, is perhaps the most deadly killer of very young calves. If the calf is severely gaunted and seems wet and soiled around the rump, don't buy it. It isn't worth the risk.

Be alert for unnatural breathing. Rapid and heavy breathing may indicate the presence of pneumonia. If you get a chance before the selling begins, get into the pen with the calf you are thinking of buying, and grab it by the ears. If her ears are cold, it may indicate she is running a temperature, a sure sign of dangerous infection.

Observe the young calf's navel. Any lump or swelling at the navel indicates navel infection or a hernia. Also, the navel may give you some clues to the calf's age. If it has a wet, raw-meat appearance, the calf is very, very young, and a poor risk. It may well not have had a single drink of colostrum.

Beware the bargain. As a novice buyer, stick to the obviously strong, healthy calves. If a calf is vigorous and healthy, runs around the pen, and kicks at the attendants, bid a few dollars more. She may be the cheapest calf in the long run. If a calf sells cheaply, be careful. There is probably a reason for it. It is better to pay $150 for a big, strong calf a week old than to pay $60 for a weak, puny, day-old calf that will sneak off to calf heaven the first time your back is turned.

Of Gender And Genetics

Your decision whether your calf is to be a heifer or a bull depends on whether you are looking for milk or meat. (A heifer calf can be raised for slaughter but usually the first cost is higher than that for a bull, so such a choice is economically unwise.) A good rule-of-thumb is to expect to pay about 80 per cent more for a heifer calf than for a bull calf of the same size and age.

There is the matter of genetics to consider. Do you want a Jersey, an Ayrshire, a Guernsey, a Brown Swiss, a Hereford, an

Angus or a Holstein? Your choice is part personal preference, part what is most commonly available in your part of the country, and part whether you are primarily interested in meat or milk or both. Contrary to general opinion, Holsteins make good meat animals, and have a very fast rate of growth. Some beef farmers prefer Holstein steers to Herefords or any of the other traditional beef breeds. In milk production, Holsteins rank at the top, at least in quantity of milk produced. However, for a family cow, you may wish to choose a Jersey, Guernsey, or Ayrshire in order to get richer milk.

Here is a little-known fact about that "rich" Jersey milk. Even though most Jerseys do produce milk with a slightly higher butterfat content than the average Holstein, the creamy color of the milk is not due to butterfat, but carotene. Carotene, a plant pigment Jerseys are unable to break down during digestion, accounts not only for their characteristic, creamy-looking milk, but also for the brown color of the cow.

When you make your decision on which breed to choose, don't forget to take into consideration the availability of that breed in your area. I know of one homesteader who read in some book that milking shorthorns are the best dual-purpose breed, so he went searching everywhere for them. In our part of the country, this breed is practically unknown, so if he ever does locate shorthorns, he will likely pay a fortune. The poor man would do better to throw his book away, and start talking with his neighbors; most of them own the best dual-purpose cattle in the world–Holsteins.

Mealtime

Small calves not only like milk, they *must* have it. There is no way they can survive on a diet of solid foods alone, because their stomachs are not developed to ruminate. Of course, if you have your own cow, you have a ready source of milk. A 100-pound calf requires about 10 to 12 pounds of whole milk a day, divided into at least two feedings. It is difficult to improve on nature; if possible, get a supply of cow's milk for at least the first week.

If you don't have a cow or some other source of cow's milk, you can resort to a commercially prepared, powdered skim milk, usually called milk replacer. Powdered skim milk for calves comes under various brand names, and is available from most feed stores for around $25 for a 20 kg bag, enough for one calf up to weaning age, at 6-8 weeks.

The milk replacer comes with directions on the bag for feeding and mixing with water, but a word of caution here. We usually go easy on the milk intake the first two days, and then gradually increase to the recommended amount. It does not hurt your calf to be on the hungry side for a day or two; it will cut down on the chances of it getting scours.

You will experience difficulty getting a very young calf to drink milk from a pail for the first few days. That is why the nipple pail was invented. A nipple pail is ideal for feeding a calf under a week old; in fact, it is even handier than trying to get the calf to suckle the cow. You can move the pail to where the calf is,

Nipple Pail
(Not available from The Pioneer Place)

hold it at any angle, and insert the nipple into the calf's mouth.

The disadvantage of using a nipple pail, rather than having the calf suckle the cow or drink directly from a pail, is that any container with rubber parts can be a possible source of bacteria. Therefore care should be taken in washing and disinfecting the pail. Nipple pails can be obtained at any feed store or co-op, and should not cost more than $15.00.

For the first three days, milk is all the food your calf needs. But after that, she should have some fresh water and some commercially mixed calf starter in front of her at all times. Actively encourage your calf to eat calf starter. At each feeding time, take a small handful of starter and edge it into the calf's mouth as she sucks your hand. The sooner you get her eating solids, the better her chance of avoiding the twin calf killers–scours and pneumonia. It is also good to supply calves with clean, leafy hay.

In A Pumpkin Shell

Besides feed and water, your calf's only other basic need is shelter. Calves require less shelter than most people think. In fact, we might take a lesson from proverbial Peter, who was fond of pumpkins. Lacking suitable housing for his wife, he made do with what he had, and put her in a pumpkin shell. The same practical approach works with calves. In fact, the trend among dairy farmers today is to put their calves outside, with only a roof and three walls for protection from the weather. This sounds unbelievable, but baby calves, several hours after birth, are put outside in subzero weather in a four-by-eight, open-ended plywood hut. They not only survive, but actually thrive. Calves do need protection from drafts, but they do not need a heated building. In fact, a warm, tight, poorly ventilated barn, stuffy from the body heat of other animals, is almost a sure place to give your calf pneumonia.

Of course, a good dry bed of straw or shavings is a must. (Dry corn cobs work great, too.) If you are interested in using an outdoor hutch to start your calf, write to the Ontario Ministry of Agriculture and Food, Information Branch, Legislative Building, Toronto M7A 1A5 and ask for fact sheet # 76-021, "Hutch Housing For Calves."

Whether you house your calf indoors or out, keep in mind the three basic requirements of a shelter: freedom from draft, good ventilation, and protection from moisture.

In Sickness And Health . . .

Two ailments probably account for 95 per cent of all sick calves–scours and pneumonia. Scours can be caused by overfeeding of milk, or by an intestinal infection due to bacteria or virus. In any case, it is advisable to cut back on the milk intake drastically for 36 hours at the first indication. However, remember that calves with scours dehydrate rapidly, and must have a daily intake of liquids, even if it is only warm water and an electrolyte mixture available from your vet. Your vet can also give you some scour medication to have on hand before you buy your calf.

If you are worried about recognizing scours, cheer up–your calf can't have a bad case, yet. When it does, you will have no doubts. Of course, it is important to detect scours and begin treatment as early as possible; but early detection can be tricky, even for professionals. Watch for excessive looseness, often to the point of wateriness. Another bad symptom is white color and a marshmallow-fluff texture. The surest way of knowing that things are serious is when your calf loses its appetite.

As for pneumonia, the first signs of it coming on are heavy breathing, running nose, and a temperature. (Normal temperature for calves, taken rectally, is around 102°F or 30°C.) The usual treatment for pneumonia is an antibiotic that your vet can supply.

If the above sounds discouraging, take heart. Most of these problems show up when people try to raise calves on a large scale, and keep 50 to 100 or more calves in one building. If you keep only a few calves and are careful to buy only strong, healthy ones, and give them reasonable care and shelter, you should seldom have a sick calf.

Solitary Confinement

Several heifer calves can be kept in one pen, but bull calves should be put in individual pens or tied out of reach of each other for the first eight weeks. Calves have a strong sucking instinct. If bull calves are not penned individually, they will frequently stand and suck each other's penile outlet and swallow urine. Soon they will begin to show signs of uremic poisoning: abnormal loss of hair and a generally unthrifty appearance. Once calves are confirmed urine suckers, the habit becomes very difficult to break. If placed into solitary confinement after this behavior is deeply ingrained, the calves will stand and bawl for hours, just as desperately as if they were being deprived of milk. The best solution is never to give the habit a chance to form.

A Four-legged Supermarket

Mrs. Jonas Stutzman, an Amish mother of seven children, has nothing but praise for the family cow. Their Guernsey not only provides them with all the milk they need, but is virtually a miniature grocery store. She puts butter on the table and cheese on the bread. The whey from the cheese feeds the hens that lay the eggs for the frying pan. The yearly calf provides the family's beef, and there is usually enough extra milk to supplement the diet of a pig, which becomes their pork. The manure from the family cow fertilizes the garden, providing an abundance of vegetables for the table. Says Mrs. Stutzman, "When I hear people who live on a few acres say they can't afford to have a cow, I have to wonder how can they afford *not* to?"

Few people with a family cow would ever again want to do without her. And one of the best ways to get on milking terms with a family cow is to grow your own. The unhurried journey from a tottery-legged calf to a gentle, cud-chewing cow can be educating, rewarding, and just plain fun. Watching the helpless calf develop into a mature heifer will give you a sense of achievement and accomplishment. And although she may never quite turn into the fabulous dream cow you had hoped for, the two years you spend growing together should ensure that she does not end up as a family nightmare, either.

Kicking Problems

Most cows, once they settle into the farm routine, will stand contentedly, quietly eating their feed while being milked. Yet there are always times when a cow needs to be restrained by force: when a new cow is not accustomed to hand milking; when milking an untrained, just-freshened heifer; or when the cow has sore teats due to an injury or chapping.

A cow has to be milked twice a day whether she likes it or not. If she does not volunteer to hold still, she needs to be restrained. There are better ways than breaking the milk stool across her back.

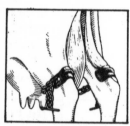

(Not available from The Pioneer Place)

Leg Hobbles: These are probably the most common and least effective restrainers. A cow that struggles violently will either kick them off, or cut ugly gashes into her legs, or both. If she cuts her legs, the kickers cannot be applied at the next milking. Their most useful function is on a quiet cow who is accustomed to them; they will prevent minor, annoying stamping. Any cow that is truly dangerous only becomes more so with these contraptions wrapped around her flying legs.

(Not available from The Pioneer Place)

Double-Hip Restrainer: This is likely the safest device, and the surest, most effective restrainer. If the cow still kicks after it is installed, it means the pressure, which is adjustable by a hand crank, isn't strong enough. There is no way a cow can lift her foot more than a few inches off the ground if these restrainers are properly tightened. The only way the cow can harm you is if you permit her to fall on top of you. The cow may throw herself a time or two; if she does, loosen the restrainer quickly and let her get up. She won't throw herself more than twice unless she is a complete bovine dunce.

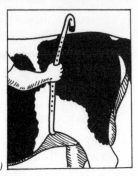

(Not available from The Pioneer Place)

Single Hip U-Hook: This effective gadget is inexpensive to buy, and simple to install. It will immobilize the leg on the side you are milking. It is almost as effective as the double hip restrainer, and much handier to use on a daily basis.

All three of the above devices are available by mail order from: Arnold-Nasco Ltd. 58 Dawson Road, Guelph, Ontario N1H 6P9. Write for their free farm and ranch catalogue, which lists many other items as well.

Home Remedies: If you don't have any of the above devices, and are not inclined to buy one, here are some home remedies that are cheaper and time-proven. If you have a second person to help you, have him raise the cow's tail straight into the air, putting on strong upward pressure at the very base of the tail; if the cow still kicks, you are not putting on enough pressure. If the cow holds still, loosen up a bit; if she struggles, reapply the pressure. You will be amazed how quickly she gets the message.

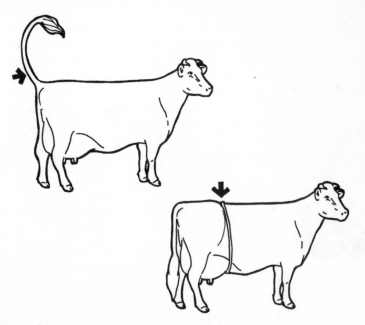

The second method is also very effective and does not require a second person. Tie a small rope tightly around the cow's belly. Make sure it crosses her back in front of her hip bones, but goes under her belly immediately forward of her udder. In a pinch, even a couple of bale ties will do the trick.

Homemade Ice Cream

Although we don't have refrigerators, we Amish probably consume more ice cream per person than any other people on earth. An ice-cream freezer is standard equipment in every Amish household. With plenty of milk, cream and eggs, and usually a supply of ice the year round, eating ice cream makes good sense for cost, taste, and nutrition. Amish children usually are not very old before they have learned to take their turn at the handle of the ice cream freezer. Most Amish families make a freezer of ice cream at least once a week. In our home, ice cream day usually comes on Saturday. We consider ice cream, not as a dessert, but as the main dish. When we have ice cream, we don't plan to have much of anything else.

How do we have ice in the middle of summer without refrigeration? Dotted throughout the community are ice houses, where ice is stored. These buildings are well insulated; inside are stored tons of ice, cut in 100 pound blocks. During the winter, usually January or February, when the ice on nearby ponds is about 14" thick, ice-making begins. The ice is cut into blocks by a circular buzz-saw-type blade mounted on buggy wheels and driven by a gasoline motor. The ice chunks are pulled out of the water with ice hooks, heaved onto sleighs pulled by two horses, and hauled to the ice house.

Although other brands of freezers can be purchased at hardware stores, all the ones we have seen other than White Mountain are flimsy, poorly built, and don't stand up to frequent use. White Mountain has been the standby in Amish homes for years; as far as we are concerned, the other makes don't exist. White Mountain freezers don't last forever, but they will outlive three or four of their plastic imitations. We are not exactly pleased with the price, as they have become quite expensive in the last five years; but there seems to be no choice but to accept it as the cost of quality in today's inflationary world.

White Mountain Ice Cream Freezer
Just like Grandma's! The world-famous triple-motion White Mountain Ice Cream Freezer is built with rugged cast-iron gear frame and dasher, and select New England white pine wood tub. Gives a lifetime of use. Every freezer comes complete with detailed instructions on care of freezer, how to make ice cream, and some recipes. Available in 4 sizes, ranging from 2-quart to 8-quart freezers.
Price range: $75-$175

The Pioneer Cheese Press

We have been on the lookout for a long time for a cheese press that we could whole-heartedly recommend to our customers. We felt such a press needed to be sturdy, durable, easy-to-clean, practical to use, and reasonably priced. All presses failed in at least one of these requirements–usually the last one, cost. Part of this is probably due to the fact that many available cheese presses are imported from Europe. The most expensive press we came across retails in the U.S. for $120. (Imagine what that would cost in Canada by the time we paid exchange on the money, duty at the border, and trucking for hundreds of miles!) And basically all this press consisted of was a stainless steel perforated hoop with a few pieces of polished hardwood above and below it. It was a good press, but we could not in conscience sell it because of the ridiculous price.

Cheese presses, by their very nature, are simple. Their only function is to exert inward and downward pressure. The only thing that is elaborate about most cheese presses is the price tag. So we designed a press, keeping it as simple as possible, yet practical, sturdy and inexpensive. Pressing pressure is supplied by weights, which you supply, stacked on top. Anything will do: bricks, several 10-pound bags of sugar, or a gallon can of washed stones. Why should we ask you to pay freight on manufactured weights when every house is full of suitable weights? If you do not have enough innovation to come up with the weights needed, you have no business making cheese anyhow!

Our press comes with two hoppers of different sizes, so you have a choice of how much cheese you make. Both hoppers are stainless steel and fit the stainless steel drainage tray. Press comes complete with polished hardwood pressing blocks that fit each hopper snugly.

Cheese Press
Our press comes with two hoppers of different sizes, so you have your choice of how much cheese you make. Both hoppers are stainless steel and fit the stainless-steel drainage tray. Press comes complete with polished hardwood pressing blocks that will fit each hopper snugly.
Price range: $40-$60

Buttermaking

Today many people who have never known any source of butter other than the grocery store, ask, "Can I make my own butter, or is that too complicated?"

Buttermaking is simple. For hundreds and even thousands of years, people have been making their own butter. In fact, butter was made for centuries before churns were invented. Milk or cream was simply shaken in a leather bag until butter resulted. Of course, the dasher churn made buttermaking convenient, and by the 1800s it was a standard household item.

Separating the Cream: If you have access to a supply of milk, there is nothing to keep you from making your own butter. The cream from about two gallons of milk will make one pound of butter. But the first step is separating the cream from the milk. With cow's milk, this is not too difficult. If milk is allowed to cool and stand undisturbed in a deep container for twelve hours or longer, the cream rises to the top in a thin layer. Then, if you are careful, you can skim most of the cream from the top without getting too much of the milk. A little milk mixed in with the cream will not hurt.

However, do not try this on homogenized milk from the supermarket. When milk has been homogenized, the butterfat globules have been so thoroughly mixed with the milk that they will not readily separate and rise to the top as cream. The let-stand-and-skim-from-the-top method will not work very well for goat's milk, either.

If you want cream from goat's milk, you need a small hand-cranked centrifugal separator. (However, unless you have a fairly large amount of milk, the purchase of such a machine may not be justified.) Centrifugal separators also do a much more accurate job of separating cow's milk, if your volume of milk justifies the use of one. (You have not only the purchase price to consider, but also the fact that these machines are a lot of work to wash and clean every day.)

Preparing the Cream: For an average-sized churn, collect cream until you have at least several quarts. Cream will keep longer if heated to almost the boiling point *before* storing. There is no need to boil, but remember, butter made from cream older than five or six days will not keep well. Now cool the cream to room temperature, and let it stand from 12 to 24 hours to "ripen" it for churning. Your cream should be cooled to 60°-65°F before churning. If your cream is too cold, some of the butterfat will stay in the buttermilk. If the cream is too warm, the butter will be soft and greasy.

Churning: The primary principle of churning is simply sufficient agitation. If you are using a dasher churn, move the wooden dasher up and down briskly, but not so vigorously that you splash out cream. If using the daisy type, turn the crank about 60 times a minute. The condition and temperature of the ripened cream will determine how soon chunks of butter will appear. The cream goes through several stages before it turns to butter, and you will soon learn what to look for. First you see tiny specks of butter; as churning continues, these form larger globs. When the buttermilk develops a slightly clearer consistency, you are ready to stop churning, and remove the butter from the buttermilk. (Do not discard the buttermilk; it can be used in baking.)

After churning is finished–average churning time varies from 10 to 20 minutes–drain off the buttermilk and wash your butter well in cool water. Drain again, and work well with a butter paddle until all the water is worked off. (If you don't have a paddle, you can make do with a wooden spoon.) Continue stirring and working the butter until no more water drains out. Add salt to taste, and stir until creamy and smooth. Shape butter in molds, and put in a cool place. If you have no refrigeration, you can keep the butter sweet by floating it in salty brine in a container on the basement floor. (Your brine is salty enough when it will float an egg.)

—prepared with the assistance of Mrs. Daniel Miller, Jr.

Daisy Churn

This ever-popular Blow hand churn has been the family butter-maker on farms and homesteads throughout the world for over 60 years. The precision, die-cast mechanism is of rust-proof alloy, and all working gears are fully enclosed. Thick, replaceable glass jars permit easy see-through while the butter is churning. Imported from England, the churn comes in 4-quart (illustrated) and 7-quart models. The 7-quart size has a square jar, rather than the round one pictured here. Otherwise they are the same type

Price range: $75-$100

Cream Separators

Cast-iron body, baked enamel paint. These manual separators have tinware of double-coated tinned steel. Electrical conversion clutch-assembly available. Comes in 2 sizes: 300 lbs. per hour and 450 lbs. per hour capacity.

Price: $500

Dasher Churn
We hunted far and wide for this attractive, 20 lb. crock dasher churn, for old-fashioned butter-making. Heavy enough to stay put while churning, yet still easy to move about. No-spill stoneware lid is designed to drain any splash-out back into the churn. Has a 3-gallon capacity, but its narrower bottom allows churning of smaller amounts. Will not dry out and leak like a wooden churn does. White with blue bands, it is 14″ high, and 9″ in diameter. Glazed finish makes it easy to keep sanitary. A quality item that will please you.
Price: around $50

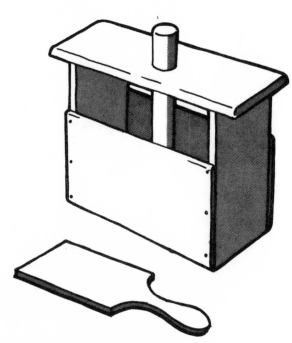

Butter Paddles
Handy wooden paddles for removing excess buttermilk after churning. Sturdy and serviceable.
Price per pair: around $5

Butter Parchments
Pre-printed wrappers to fit our butter mold. Wraps one-pound blocks in a tasteful, attractive parchment with blue color and design.
Price per 100 sheets: around $5

Butter Mold
All-wood, one-pound, adjustable molds for easy shaping and molding of butter. Smooth finish for ready cleaning.
Price: about $10

7

A Ringing Message

Bells have a long history, dating back to biblical times. They have been used for warning of fire, calling for help, announcing a death, or summoning worshippers to church. Bells vary in size, from tiny ones that weigh less than an ounce to the massive, 200-ton King Bell, cast in 1735 in Russia.

 We have worked hard to find good bells at reasonable prices and feel that we have a fair selection.

(Not available from The Pioneer Place)

Farm Bell
Our farm bell is all cast iron, so it has that old-fashioned ring. This is not a machine-made product. Each bell is cast from individual sand molds, so bells vary somewhat in exact weight and measurement. The ring of this bell can be heard for a mile or two. A large bell, it measures about 15" in diameter, and weighs 50 lbs.
Price range: $80-$100

Post Bell
This handy-sized post bell has a clear ring, measures up to 8¾" in diameter, and weighs about 18 lbs.
Price range: $45-$60

Steer Head Bell

We sell a lot of these bells. Wall-mounting, this cast-iron bell differs from the farm bell and the post bell in that this bell does not swing. To ring it, you tie a cord to the gong and pull the gong against the sides of the bell. A number of people have told us that they have put this bell up at their front door as a door bell. Measures 6" in diameter, and weighs around 10 lbs.
Price range: $30-$40

Ship's Bell

This brass ship's bell is beautifully impressive. Diameter is 7", and it weighs 7 lbs.
Price range: $85-$100

Large School Bell

This is a large hand bell, 5½" in diameter, and 12" high overall. Brass, with varnished handle. Has a loud, clear ring.
Price range: $45-$55

Small School Bell

Here is another school bell of polished brass, with a beautifully carved wooden handle. This bell isn't really small—only in comparison with our large school bell. This one is 4" in diameter, and stands 8" tall, overall.
Price range: $35-$45

Part Two: Home

8 Warm Friends

(Not available from
The Pioneer Place)

Our family consists of Mom and Dad, five boys and one cookstove. Well, maybe that's taking it a bit far, but the cookstove does seem almost like a member of the family. We certainly do not think of it as a thing of cold steel and nuts and bolts.

There is, of course, every reason for our affection. She greets us in the morning with radiant warmth and aromatic cheer. The air is moist with the aroma of herbal tea steaming gently in the humming teakettle. From the faithful cast-iron pan on the stove top comes the smell of melting butter, a sure sign it's time to fry the fresh eggs for breakfast. The pot of oatmeal bubbles lazily, and the slices of homemade bread toast above the glowing embers.

What luxury we enjoy, being able to come into the house on a cold winter day and stand by the kitchen stove to warm chilled fingers and numb cheeks! Especially if it is the one day of the week when the kitchen air is heavy with the mouth-watering smell of bread in the oven. The boys wait and watch eagerly as Mother pulls out the loaves, bulging with wholesome goodness beneath the steaming crusts, brown and chewy. Occasionally, if they have been good and Mother is in an indulgent mood, they are rewarded with a slice of bread while it is still warm. When the loaf is tender from the oven, fragile as a newborn, slicing it into proper pieces is nearly impossible. The odd-shaped slices, thick here, thin there, a bit crushed and doughy, add to the special occasion. Top them off with country butter and fresh homemade strawberry jam, and there is not much more a boy could wish for.

In the evenings, coming into the house with mittens wet from making a snowman or having a snowball fight, the boys head straight for the comfort of the kitchen stove. There is no better spot to dry cold, clinging mitts. Next morning those mitts will be transformed. Granted, they may be a bit stiff and unbending for a few moments, but they will soon flex up again, and be warm and cosy on small fingers. What miracles that cookstove can perform! No wonder all of us have come to admire it!

On many a winter evening, when the north wind howls and

the snowbanks are high against the front door, we have a family gathering around the cookstove in the kitchen. If we have hand cranked a gallon or two of ice cream in the old White Mountain freezer, we eat the evening meal in an improvised fashion nestled around the cookstove. We open the oven door to let out as much heat as possible, jostle a bit for position (the winner gets to prop his feet in the oven door), and occasionally stir up the coals or add a piece of dry wood. Then we sit back and enjoy the conflicting sensation of toasty warmth on the outside, and delicious, almost numbing cold on the inside as the ice cream melts in our mouths.

And talk of a cure for cold feet! Blessed is the boy who can come home from school on a bitter winter day, pull up a rocking chair and prop his stocking feet on the oven door of a kitchen stove. Nothing can be right with the world when feet are cold; and not everything can be amiss when they are being made cosy at the side of a kitchen stove.

In years to come, when our boys look back on each member of the family, we hope they will not forget the loyal cookstove.

Of course, a cookstove in the kitchen has much more than sentimental value. It makes a lot of practical sense. In a world of rising fuel prices and soaring hydro bills, wood heat is coming into its own. And a good kitchen stove is the most sensible wood heater ever invented. A space heater provides heat, which is fine. But a cookstove provides heat, as well as a place to fry the bacon, boil the porridge, and bake the bread.

Cookstoves have been around a long time, and have remained largely unchanged for years. Most of the cookstoves on the market today differ very little from the one Grandma used, except that today's manufacturers skimp on quality and gouge on price. For some reason, the airtight revolution that hit the woodheat industry in the living room bypassed the kitchen.

For years we looked for a good airtight cookstove, but with little success. We had a lot of people asking us to recommend a good, serviceable cookstove, but we were unhappy with the performance of the available stoves. Finally we decided to design our own.

We worked for months on the design. We looked at many older models and examined all the present-day productions. We gleaned ideas, but found no stove that we felt was good enough. The world deserved a better cookstove.

We read everything we could lay our hands on concerning wood stoves in general, and cookstoves in particular. We talked with manufacturers, distributors, and wholesalers, getting their opinions of various features we were considering. We also relied heavily on our own experience and the expertise of members of our community who had grown up with cookstoves, and cooked on them all their lives.

The problem was that most cookstoves, because they are not airtight, are shamefully inefficient, allowing much of the heat to escape up the flue. Fire boxes tend to be small, so many cookstoves are unable to hold a good steady fire for any length of time, and require constant refueling. Banking the fire for an overnight burn is out of the question; each morning you need to build a fire in a cold stove, and many cold stoves tend to smoke. Soon the kitchen ceiling takes on an ominous color.

Write to us for a price list, specifications of size, weight, etc., and availability in your area.

Price: $950

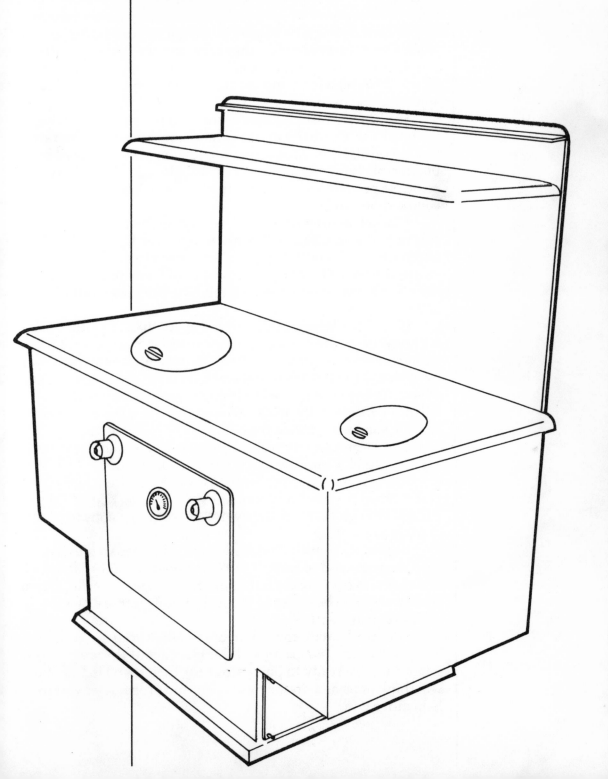

We designed and redesigned, working on the blueprint far into the night, after our regular work was finished. We built a trial model and tested it extensively to determine whether our concept was workable. It took time, but we finally made it—the Pioneer Maid—a downdraft airtight cookstove. Our stove has many features no other cookstove has. A single-piece welded steel top ensures a smooth surface. An airtight firebox makes possible a degree of control Grandma never dreamed of. A quick twist of the twin draft-control knobs instantly tames a roaring fire; in fact, it can come near to putting it out entirely if you wish. Twirl the knobs the other way, and the fire leaps into action again. You can have the back portion of the stove top adjusted for high heat and the front portion for low heat, all by adjusting the twin knobs.

Our downdraft principle permits all the air to enter the firebox from above the grates. This means the air intake rate remains entirely in your control. You won't be frustrated by ash buildup plugging the air intake vents. Also, the downdraft principle permits a good build-up of live embers, so that combustion can be complete.

Our ultra-large firebox cuts down on the need for extra splitting of wood, and allows you to bank the fire to burn overnight. In the morning you do not need to awaken to a cold room, search for kindling, and start a fire, only to get smoke on the ceiling. You simply turn a knob. The fire jumps out of bed and into action.

Our extra-large oven has more space than any other oven we know of; it also has a circulating interior-heat control that is a totally new concept in oven temperature. It does away with an oven that is too hot at the top and too cold at the bottom. Our oven circulator is designed to keep the heat more evenly balanced. Incidentally, it also allows you to smell more quickly what is happening inside the oven.

Our large-capacity water reservoir and humidifier is built of stainless steel, guaranteed never to rust or corrode.

Add it all up–an extra-large firebox, huge oven, giant reservoir–extra space and roominess where you need it. Yet our compact design restricts the overall stove dimensions to a manageable size.

But we do admit our stove is heavy. Be prepared to have four men on hand to carry it into the house. Quality carries a lot of weight–that's why we built our stove the way we did. Other cookstoves may be easier to move, but none is more of a pleasure to live with.

Go ahead, invite the neighbors in when your stove arrives. They will grunt and groan and complain about the weight. But when they are ready to buy a stove for their own kitchen, they will think of us and of our cookstove–and probably of you to help move it in.

Common-Sense Canning

9

—by Elizabeth Miller

Several years ago, Mike and Susan sold their house in the city and built a new home in the country. Being ardent back-to-the-landers, they eyed their big back yard and planned a garden. Susan grew up in the country, so gardening was not an altogether new experience, although she had been away from it for a number of years. With what she remembered and what Mike learned from gardening manuals, their garden thrived and yielded bountifully.

By the middle of the summer, Mike and Susan realized they had misjudged how many vegetables their family could consume. "We could keep up with the corn, if it weren't for the green beans and summer squash and all the other vegetables that are ready at the same time," Susan lamented. "We looked into canning, but decided it wasn't for us. Eighty dollars for a pressure canner! For the little bit of canning we'd do, it's not worth it.

"The articles we read said pressure canning was the only way you can be sure to kill botulism and all those germs that cause food poisoning."

I kept thinking about what Susan had said about canning. Even though I have been helping to can fruits and vegetables since I was old enough to stand on a small wooden bench and wash jars for my mother, I couldn't remember ever having read anything on how to can food safely. What if I had been doing it wrong all these years?

A few weeks after Mike and Susan's visit I found an article in *Reader's Digest* on safe canning methods. I read it eagerly–not because I wanted to learn how to can, but because I wanted reassurance that I had been doing it right. The article did not make me feel better at all. I was amazed that something as simple and safe as home canning could be made to sound so complicated and dangerous.

Just how great is the danger of botulism, that deadly food poison? Even though the Amish people can thousands of quarts of food each year, there have been no known cases of botulism among them. While it is true that the spores that cause botulism cannot be destroyed except by extreme heat, such as that attained through pressure canning, the danger can be eliminated. Any harmful bacteria can be destroyed by cooking food for five to seven minutes after it has been taken from the jars. This is true of both non-acid vegetables and meats, the most likely places for these spores to be found.

In spite of the article, I continue to do it my way. Perhaps I shouldn't call it "my way" because it really isn't mine; it's my mother's way. I learned to can from her. She learned it from her mother, who learned it from her mother. Since most of the Amish people raise as much of their own food as possible, canning is an art that is carefully handed down from generation to generation. Every devoted, frugal mother teaches her daughters the best way to preserve food value and natural flavor through canning.

I am one of those fortunate daughters. Each summer I worked side by side with my mother, learning by doing. We canned until all the jars were full; then, if necessary, we bought more jars. As the family grew, we needed more and more canned food. Then, as all families do, ours reached its peak and became smaller. Did we then have extra jars, sitting idly in the basement? Not at all. As each child left to establish a home of his or her own, a certain number of jars (filled ones, of course) left as well. This helped to tide the young couple over until the next gardening and canning season, and provided them with some jars to refill with their own produce.

The possibilities of home canning are almost unlimited. If you come to our basement with me, I'll show you nearly all the canned foods you can buy at the supermarket, plus a few more: canned strawberries for one, canned chili soup for another.

Our canned food falls into three major categories–fruits, vegetables, and meats–plus some minor and related ones such as soups, relishes, sauces and broths. And the cost per jar? They don't have price tags, but they don't have to tell me they are far cheaper than anything I can buy at the store.

Take sweet corn, one of our favorite vegetables, for example. A package of seeds costs around a dollar. If it does well, it will easily produce twenty-five to thirty pints of corn. Snap lids cost forty-five cents a dozen if bought in large quantities. That adds up to a little more than two dollars for thirty pints of corn–less than seven cents per pint.

But what about all the hard work that goes with canning, not to mention planting, weeding and caring for the garden? Gardening and canning are indeed hard work, but for me they are enjoyable and satisfying. Knowing that I have an abundance of good, wholesome food without preservatives or artificial additives is a reward I cannot measure in dollars and cents.

Looking Through the Glass

The ordinary glass jar is so common today that it is hard to believe that canning is less than one hundred and fifty years old. Preserving perishable food by canning was unknown until the early 1800s; and then for the first fifty years, most cans were made of tin. This never became practical for home canning, because machinery was required to seal the cans properly.

In 1908, a man named John L. Mason invented a glass

container with a screw-on top, which proved satisfactory for home canning. His jar used a one-piece lid with a rubber ring to make it airtight. In 1909, Alexander Kerr made a metal cap with a rubber gasket. A few years later, he came out with the two-piece snap lids that are commonly used today.

The glass jar has remained virtually unchanged for nearly seventy-five years, perhaps because it is hard to improve upon. Here's why:

1. *Sanitation.* The secret of successful canning lies in killing all the harmful bacteria in the food and then placing a barrier between the food and other bacteria. Canning was discovered when it was proven that bacteria need air in order to grow. Thus, an airtight container was the way to preserve food. The glass jar is not only airtight, it is easy to clean. It has no seams in which bacteria can lodge. The glass is nonporous, so a quick swirl in boiling water will sterilize the jar.

2. *Transparency.* Glass jars allow us to look in without breaking the seal. I'm sure that, if a housewife could not stand and survey her shelves filled with jars of peas, corn, peaches, berries, beets, beans and meat, she would not feel the same satisfaction in her work. Not only can we see what's in the jar without opening it, we can see how good it's going to be. If food loses its color, it will lose its flavor as well. If mold forms on the top, we know something is happening that shouldn't be. If the juice gets bubbly, the food has spoiled (as bubbling is a sign of fermentation, which causes food to turn sour).

The transparency of jars has another advantage: we can see if they are clean. Hold a jar to the light. It should sparkle and shine. In some cases the outside of the jar may become tinted from water containing a lot of iron. This can hardly be avoided, but if you see stains and traces of former contents on the inside, the jar needs to be washed a little better.

3. *Durability.* Jars can be used again and again. Sure, they break if they are handled roughly; but if we treat them with respect, our children and grandchildren will be using the jars we leave behind.

When shopping for jars, today's customer will find a variety of sizes and shapes: half-pint, pint, pint-and-a-half, quart and two-quart. Then there is the choice between wide-mouth and regular jars. All can be purchased by the dozen in nearly any grocery store. They come complete with snap lids and sealing bands.

Besides buying jars at the store, there are other ways of obtaining them. Almost half the wide-mouth jars we have were bought one by one, filled with Miracle Whip salad dressing. The article I read on canning said one should never use these jars because the glass is too thin and will not withstand the heat of processing. I'm sorry, but as I didn't know any better, I have been using these jars all along. Until they start breaking on me, I plan to continue to do so. Since they haven't broken during the last ten years, I hardly expect them to during the next ten. In fact, I keep the possibility of reusing the jar in mind when I shop for food. I have often paid ten cents a quart more for salad dressing because it came in a nice reusable wide-mouth jar. With jars priced at around four dollars a dozen, a ten-cent jar is a bargain.

Another source of cheap jars is an auction sale. However, be careful. You may end up with the "Crown" jars that were popular in Canada a generation ago. They are made of heavier glass and today's common snap lids do not fit them. However, special lids are available in Canada. They are a three-piece affair, consisting of a glass dome, a rubber ring, and a metal band. The glass dome and the band are reusable. The rubber ring should be replaced each time.

Shopping for lids is not difficult. Even though jars come in a variety of sizes and shapes, the openings have been standardized so there are only three sizes: narrow, regular and wide.

The narrow-mouth jars are known as #63s. The jars are no longer on the market, but the lids are still available. Most of us have a number of these jars around and use them for tomato juice, soup and other liquid foods. They can be used for anything, but they are harder than other jars to fill.

The regulars are the most common ones. They are the most practical for nearly all canning purposes.

Then there are the wide-mouth jars, which have an opening about three inches in diameter. These jars are convenient for meat, especially chicken that is canned on the bone. They are also used for very large peach halves and sometimes for pears. However, since both the jars and the lids are more expensive than the regulars, they should not be used when the others will serve the purpose as well.

Like any other product, jars and lids come under different brand names–Kerr, Ball Dome, Mason, Atlas, Bernardin, and many others. Fortunately, they are interchangeable. The companies did the canning world a big favor when they got together and standardized their products. As a result, a Kerr lid fits a Mason jar, and vice versa.

Size is not the only thing lids have in common: all are dome lids. If you examine one closely, you will see that it is slightly domed. When the jar becomes airtight, that dome is pulled down. Often you will hear a smart little snap when this happens, although many domes are of the silent seal type. *How* it is pulled down is not important. *That* it is pulled down is very important. It is your assurance that the jar has sealed.

There are rare occasions when a lid has sealed, but has not pulled its dome down. When it is touched lightly with the tip of the finger, there will be a snap and it will pop down and stay: that jar has sealed. But if you must apply pressure, it is not sealed. You might be able to make the dome stay down, but that will not seal the jar. The food will spoil within a week.

When a jar has been sealed for twenty-four hours, the sealing band should be removed and stored in a dry place. If it is kept on the jar, it will rust or corrode. Removing it carefully will not harm the seal; not removing it will not conserve the seal.

Pressure, Non-pressure and Steam Canning

One of the most confusing things about home canning is the question of pressure or non-pressure canning. Fruits should not be pressure canned as the process will overcook them; but with vegetables and meats, every home canner has the freedom of choice.

In order to choose, you must understand the differences. A pressure canner is a heavy utensil with a clamp-on lid. There is a gauge on top of the lid to help the user regulate the pressure within, and a safety valve to eliminate the danger of excess pressure.

Only a small amount of water is used in this process. By sealing the steam inside the container, the temperature rises far beyond the boiling point, cooking the food faster than would otherwise be possible. Processing time is cut about in half for meats and even more for vegetables. This conserves fuel as well as time.

The main disadvantage of pressure canning is the initial cost of the canner, which is several times that of a non-pressure utensil.

While the non-pressure canner processes your food more slowly, it is a simpler method. Any utensil that is deep enough to hold your jars and has a lid that fits can be used as a canner. You should have a canning rack to put in the bottom, but several layers of wire mesh or fencing cut to fit will serve the purpose well. All you need is something to allow the water to circulate between the jars and the bottom of the container. Extra sealing bands or even a heavy layer of old rags will do.

Special canning utensils can be bought at nearly any hardware store. They usually come complete with canning rack and lid. Water bath canning equipment is safe and simple to use, and inexpensive to buy. The drawback is the lengthy processing time required.

Although unheard of when I was a girl helping Mother, recent years have introduced a sensible compromise solution, the steam canner. This utensil resembles an upside-down canner. A small amount of water is put in the shallow bottom part and the jars are set on a rack above the water. A deep lid is placed over the jars. The food is heated by the steam of the boiling water and the processing time is reduced.

First costs of steam-canning equipment compare favorably with that of the water-bath method, and processing, although not as rapid as pressure canning, takes only about half the time of a water bath. All in all, steam canning seems to be both safe and practical.

Fruits that Taste Fresh

There are many different fruits and many ways of canning each one. No wonder the novice home canner is confused! However, we will concentrate on two basic methods of canning fruits.

1. *The open-kettle method.* The secret of successful canning is destroying harmful bacteria. Bringing food to the boiling point does this. The open-kettle method of canning simply involves preparing food as you would to serve it fresh, then heating it to

a *full* boil. While it is boiling hot, ladle it into a sterilized jar and close immediately. As the food in the jar cools, it contracts enough to draw down the seal, making the container airtight.

2. *The cold-packing method.* This is just what the name suggests. The fruit is peeled, pitted, stemmed and washed. Then it is packed into the jars cold and raw. A syrup of sugar and water is added, and the jars are closed. They are then set into the canner. Enough water is added to cover the jars up to the sealing bands. The water is then brought to the boiling point and held there for eight to ten minutes. The water around the jars should boil gently. Boiling fruit jars too hard or too long overcooks the fruit, causing it to become soft, discolored and tasteless.

However, it is important that the fruit reaches boiling point. The juice will not bubble like it would in an open kettle, but the fruit will shrink and rise to the top of the jar. For example, when peaches or pears have risen at least three-quarters of an inch, it is safe to assume that they have reached the boiling point. Berries shrink much more.

When you feel the jars are "done," turn off the burner and remove the canner lid. Let the jars set a few minutes, then remove them from the water and set them in a draft-free place to cool. Do not tighten the sealing bands yet, or you may interfere with the sealing of the jar.

By this time you should be hearing "snaps" and "pings" as the jars seal. This is music to the home canner's ear. If there are still domes that have not pulled down after thirty minutes, set the jars upside down. They should then be kept in this position until they are completely cooled.

As a rule, cold packing is the better method for peaches, pears, blueberries, applesauce, grapefruit, cherries and plums. Fruits that are very soft and juicy, such as strawberries, raspberries and blackberries, are better when they are canned by the open-kettle method, as they can be preserved in their own juice, rather than in a sugar-and-water syrup. If they are canned by the cold-packing method, they tend to be lighter in color and the juice is more watery. They also shrink drastically. A jar filled with berries becomes one half berries and one half juice during processing.

Nearly all canned fruits require some sugar, although fully ripe fruit (preferably tree or vine ripened) will not need as much sugar as unripe fruit. There are three standard recipes for fruit syrups:

> Thin syrup: three parts water to one part sugar
> Medium syrup: two parts water to one part sugar
> Heavy syrup: one part water to one part sugar

The syrup does not need to be boiled, but heating it will help dissolve the sugar. Whenever possible, part of the water should be replaced by the fruit's own juice.

**A Variety
of Vegetables**

Vegetable canning is much like fruit canning, but there are some important differences. For one thing, bringing vegetables to the boiling point is not enough. Just as vegetables must be tenderized by cooking before we eat them, the same thing must take place in the canning process.

The processing time for vegetables, using the water-bath non-pressure method, is usually three hours after the water has begun to boil. (It should boil gently, with the burner turned low.) However, processing times for both non-pressure and pressure canning vary with climate and altitude. The higher you live above sea level, the longer the food must be processed.

For the beginner, the cold-packing, non-pressure method is the simplest. The rules are basically the same for all common vegetables–corn, peas, green beans and lima beans. You simply prepare the food just as you would if you were going to cook it for dinner, but instead of cooking it, you pack it loosely in sterilized jars. Add a teaspoon of salt per quart of vegetables before you fill the jar with water. If you're canning beans or sweet corn, also add a half teaspoon of vinegar or lemon juice. As these are non-acid foods, certain kinds of harmful bacteria thrive in them. A bit of vinegar, lemon juice or even a slice of raw tomato will add the needed acid to kill the bacteria without altering the flavor. Put on the lids, and the jars are ready for their hot-water bath. Handle them as you would fruit, except for lengthening the processing time.

Even though canning vegetables can seem simple, it is not always so. People seem to have more trouble with vegetable spoilage than with fruit. The jars seal, but after ten days to two weeks they lose their seal, the dome bulges up, and a foul-smelling liquid spews out. This is always a disheartening sight. If one jar does it, chances are others will, too. What happened?

It could have been a number of things. One reason canned vegetables spoil is because of improper handling before canning. (I would never buy vegetables at a store or vegetable stand and can them.) The faster they are put into jars after picking, the better is their chance of keeping well.

If vegetables must be picked one day and canned the next, they should be spread out in a cool place. If they are kept in a basket, the middle heats up. It may be ever so slightly, but it might be enough to let harmful bacteria grow.

Sweet corn is one vegetable I was taught to be extra careful with. We picked it while it was still wet with dew, and canned it as fast as possible. Sometimes we picked it the evening before and spread it out in the yard overnight. Early the next morning we were out husking the ears and picking off the silk. We shivered, because the dew on an early autumn morning is something we didn't really care to take on our laps, but we always had good canned sweet corn with little spoilage.

They say that vegetables should be in the jars two hours after they've been picked. This isn't always possible, especially if you're by yourself and have picked a bushel of peas! But "the sooner the better" is a good rule to follow. Food that has been picked awhile not only gives harmful bacteria a good start, but it loses both flavor and food value.

Headaches

No matter how many precautions we take, home canning is never completely free of headaches. Sometimes, seemingly without reason, a can will break while in the hot-water bath. Being human, I need someone or something to blame when this happens. Even if that someone is me, I need to put my finger on what I did wrong. Maybe I packed the jars too tightly. Some foods, such as partially dried beans, expand while cooking, and the pressure inside could burst the jar.

Placing a very cold jar in hot water, or vice versa could break it, too. A sudden change of temperature can cause the glass to break. This is a danger particularly with open-kettle canning. The jar should be warm, preferably fresh out of the hot-water rinse that sterilized it. It is never wise to hold the jar you are filling with hot food, lest it break and scald you. Always set it in a pan beside the kettle you are ladling from.

Jars may break if they are weakened through rough handling. They get barely noticeable hairline cracks, weak spots that will not withstand the pressure the jar is exposed to during food processing.

Next to breaking jars, the biggest headache is jars that fail to seal. The first thing I look for is a chip along the sealing edge. It may be ever so tiny, but if it will let air escape the jar will not seal. At our house, a chipped jar is a broken jar, and it is discarded.

Jars may not seal if the contents do not reach the boiling point. The first year I did much canning on my own, I had a Coleman hotplate. I turned the burner wide open, and it did not take long to bring the water in the canner to boiling point. Being cautious to not over-cook the fruit I was canning, I removed the jars after eight minutes, but as many as half did not seal. That's a very poor average. Then a friend pointed out that, although the water around the jars reached the boiling point rapidly, the fruit within the jars took longer. When I turned the burner down and heated the water more gently, the jars sealed.

Foreign matter between the glass brim and the sealing rubber will also hinder sealing. A tiny kernel of corn, a speck of peaches or a bit of string bean will be enough to keep a jar from sealing. The tops of the jars should be carefully wiped with a clean, damp cloth before the lids are put on.

No matter how careful we are and how many tricks we learn in the canning trade, there will always be a certain number of jars that won't seal. (I've never kept close track of them, but I would guess maybe one out of twenty-five.) But even if a jar doesn't seal, the food isn't wasted. If we're going to do more canning in the next day or so, we'll run it through another hot-water bath the next time. If it doesn't seal the second time, we give up and eat the contents. If we have reason to think the jar is at fault, we discard it. It could be one of those odd "grocery store" jars we aren't supposed to be using in the first place, and the lid may not quite fit.

An Endless Cycle

If the jars in our basement could speak, they would have an interesting story to tell. We have "young" jars we bought ten years ago and "old" ones that have served their purpose for several generations. But to us there is no difference. Jars do not age. They just faithfully keep on doing their duty, season after season. They take numerous trips, downstairs and up, upstairs and down. From full to empty and from empty to full.

We often refer to summertime as the canning season. It starts with rhubarb, the very first fruit of spring, and goes on beyond the first killing frost in autumn. This is indeed the busiest canning season; but, at our house, we work with jars and canned food the year round. Carrying empty jars upstairs to the storage room is a weekly chore. Carrying filled jars up from the basement is a daily joy.

By spring and early summer, the canned-goods shelves in the basement resemble the shelves of a food store going out of business. There is only a quart of this and a few pints of that, and we need to plan our meals accordingly. We eat more peaches because the berries are nearly all gone, and we try to finish up the last raspberries before the fresh ones ripen in the garden.

Meanwhile, the shelves upstairs are filled with empty jars, and we have to store some away in boxes. But soon the strawberries ripen and the peas are ready, and we bring down the empty jars and refill them. By fall, the shelves in the basement groan beneath their load. They have their own story to tell, the story of a bountiful harvest, of prosperity and security from want and hunger, and of mothers and daughters working side by side to preserve not only food, but a way of life.

Copper Wash Boiler
This high-grade wash boiler is built for us by the company that pioneered the original copper boiler in grandfather's day. Excellent for water-bath canning, it will fit over two burners. Boiler holds almost 10 imp. gal. Complete with lid.
Length 22". Width 12". Height 13".
Price: under $50

Traditional Canning Jars

For anything needing an airtight container. Simple old- fashioned charm of an era before cardboard and plastic. Great for use as cannisters, and for storing dried foods or leftovers. Ideal if you like to give jars of your home canning as gifts. With glass lids, rubbers and bails, they are absolutely airtight.
Price range: $1.75 and up, each

White Mountain Cherry Pitter

Handily removes pits without crushing the fruit. Thin plunger extracts pits with little damage to fruit. No springs; nothing to get out of order. Easy to operate; has plunger finger guard. Cast iron, tinned inside and out. Recommended for all purposes.
Price: under $40

Chop-Rite Cherry Stoner

This heavy-duty cherry stoner is especially good for sour cherries for use in jams or other foods in which it does not matter if the fruit is hurt. The manufacturers say "Pits without hurting fruit," but we find this less than honest. It can do extensive damage to fruit, and does not pit sweet cherries well. However, it does perform well with sour cherries when undamaged fruit is not required. It cleans easily, will not rust, and has no rubber washer to wear out.
Price: under $30

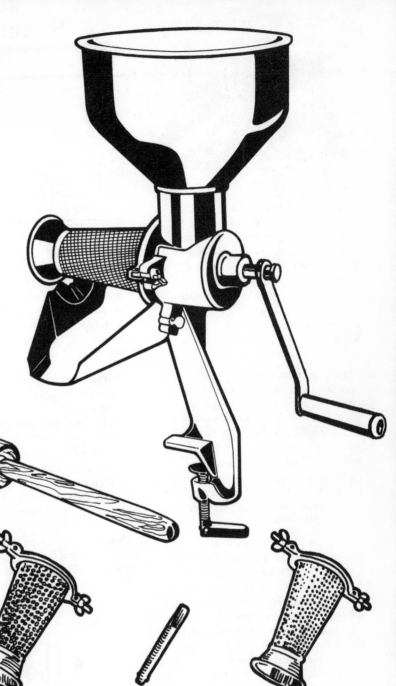

Victorio Strainer

Makes tomato sauce, catsup, apple sauce, fruit purees, baby food, diet foods. Perfect for canning and freezing.

Made of durable light-weight cast aluminum, this strainer has a unique large-capacity feature. Capacity is determined by the size of the spiral and screen, not by the size of the hopper. The larger the diameter of the spiral and the spaces between the ribs, the faster you can strain foods. No peeling or coring. Separates juices and pulp from skin and seeds.

Comes with plastic worm auger, hardwood push stick, and directions for assembly and use. Comes apart easily for cleaning. Trouble-free nylon spiral and hopper cannot dent or rust. No plating to peel; easy to wash. Not affected by boiled fruit and vegetables.
Price range: $35-$45

Accessories

Grape Spiral

A shorter spiral to process grapes without jamming. Use with standard Victorio screen.
Price: $8-$10

Pumpkin Screen

A coarse (1/8") mesh screen for processing pumpkin and squash. Puree will be skinless and stringless. Use with standard Victorio spiral.
Price: $10-$12

Pulley Shaft

Interchangeable shaft for attaching a pulley, for those who want to motorize their strainer.
Price: $5

Berry Screen

A fine (3/64") mesh screen for processing berries for jellies, etc. The small holes will separate the seeds from the juice. Use with standard Victorio spiral. Elderberries cannot be processed with this screen.
Price: $10-$12

The Juicer

Enjoy the nutritional benefits of fresh, natural juices. This easy-to-use juicer quickly steam-extracts delicious juices, syrups and cider. It's also ideal for steam-cooking meats, chicken, fish and fresh vegetables. Made of rugged, safe procelain on steel, it's lightweight and easy to clean. The non-porous Graniteware surface resists acids, stains and odors.

How it works: The juicer creates steam, which opens the food cells, condenses the steam created, and drips it through the food, extracting a flavorful juice. The juice collects in the retention section, where it is steam-cooked. The natural food content is preserved, as the extract is never boiled. Juices can be bottled and sealed directly from the juicer. No need to reheat.

The juicer also doubles as a steamer-cooker. You can steam complete meals while preserving full natural flavors, vitamins and minerals. Excellent for clams, lobsters, crabs, mussels and sausages. Also steams fresh corn on the cob, green vegetables, potatoes for mashing and apples for applesauce. Works great for steamed puddings, buns and cakes, too.
Price: $50-$60

Steaming time table

Fruit	Approx. Min. To Steam	Fruit	Approx. Min. To Steam
Apples	80	Peaches	60
Apricots	60	Pears	70
Blackberries	50	Plums	60
Cherries	60	Prunes	60
Cranberries	70	Raspberries	60
Currants	60	Rhubarb	70
Elderberries	60	Strawberries	60
Gooseberries	80	Tomatoes	60
Grapes	60		

Steaming Timetable

These times may vary according to the variety of fruit, ripeness, altitude and intended use. If fruit is to be used for jams, preserves, sauces, etc., the extraction time may be shortened slightly so the extract will be moister and retain more flavor and color. Fruit may be gently stirred or folded with a wooden spoon once or twice during the extraction time so the steam will work evenly throughout the fruit.

Homemade Catsup

6 qts. fresh tomatoes
4 cups sugar
1½ tablespoons catsup spice
3 tablespoons salt
3 cups apple vinegar
¾ teaspoon red pepper
1 teaspoon dry mustard
2 tablespoons cinnamon
4-5 tablespoons corn starch

Dice tomatoes. Add all ingredients except corn starch. Stir well, and boil for 2 hours. Put sauce through a Victorio Strainer. Thicken with corn starch. Boil for 10 minutes. Seal in sterilized bottles or canning jars.

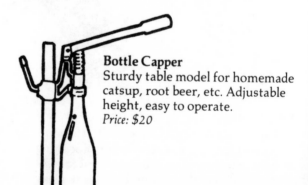

Bottle Capper

Sturdy table model for homemade catsup, root beer, etc. Adjustable height, easy to operate.
Price: $20

Bottle Crowns

Standard bottle caps with plastic seal. Sold 144 to a carton.
Price: $2 per carton

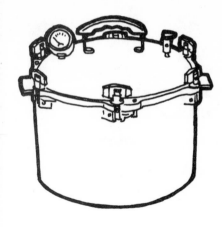

Pressure Canners

The All-American steam-pressure canners are the only ones available that have all the features necessary for efficiency, safety and long life. The heavy-guage kettle is of heavy cast aluminum. The exclusive "metal-to-metal" seal eliminates gaskets. Six sturdy wing-nut clamps hold the precision-machined lid tight for an exact fit.

A precision-geared steam guage has a large dial for easy and accurate temperature and pressure readings. The steam-pressure control valve automatically releases excess steam before a dangerous level of pressure can develop. A second safety valve is included as an extra safety measure.

Each canner can be used as a pressure cooker and for cold packing. Each comes with a canning rack and 64-page instruction booklet.

The All-American comes in 5 sizes:
7-qt. model: makes a splendid pressure cooker, but it's a bit small for most canning jobs. Great for cooking pot roasts, steamed chicken, quick-cooking soy beans and vegetables for family dinners. Will hold 4 pint jars.

Diameter 9". Height 6".
10-qt. model: Will hold 7 pint jars or 4 quart jars. Diameter 10½". Height 8".
15-qt. model: Will hold 10 pint jars or 7 quart jars or 12 #2 cans. Diameter 13". Height 8".
21-qt. model: Will hold 18 pint jars or 7 quart jars or 4½-gal. jars or 18 #2 cans. Diameter 13". Height 11".
41-qt. model: Will hold 24 pint jars or 16 quart jars or 6 ½-gal. jars. Diameter 15". Height 14".
Price range for five models: $50-$180

Steam Canner

Steam canners use less water than water-bath canners, and preheat in half the time. Can process 1 to 7 quart jars. For use with tomatoes, fruits and other naturally acidic foods. Rugged porcelain on steel; comes with sturdy aluminum steamer rack. Cover doubles as 15-qt. soup and stock pot.
Price: $30-$35

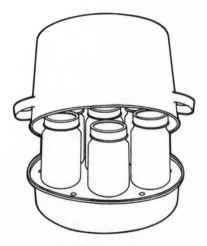

10 The Butcher

—by Daniel Miller, Jr.

We did our own butchering as far back as I can remember, and for quite a few years we did custom butchering for other people. There are, of course, many different ways of dressing an animal, and many different animals. However, since more pigs than any other animal are dressed by the home butcher, I will use it as an example.

The first thing is the scalding. Nowadays, a lot of people skin the hogs instead, but this loses a lot of lard. The ideal scalding tank is an oblong affair designed to have a fire beneath it to keep the water hot during use. However, where such a tank is not available, a 45-gal. drum with the top cut out works fine, too. If the hog is too big to fit into the drum, dip her in head first, then turn her around and dip her back end in. But be sure to have hot water on hand to add when changing the hog around; the original water will have cooled off too much for a good scald. Add a shovelful of wood ashes to the water; it makes the hair come off easier.

The temperature of the scalding water is very important. If you can dip your finger in and out three times in a row, the water is just right. (Scalding too hard is worse than not enough.) If a hog scraper is not available, use a dull knife or the back side of a hand saw to scrape the hair off. When all the hair that you can loosen has been removed, take a sharp knife and shave off what is left. This can easily be done after the hog is hanging.

Now take the head off about two inches behind the ears. Cut the head into two pieces from the mouth on back, and take the tongue out. Then trim off all the meat. This is a good job for the women while the men go on with gutting the hog.

Cut the hog open down the front to the rib cage. Be careful not to cut deeper than just the skin, so you don't cut the intestines. A good way to prevent this is to run one hand along the inside of the skin as you cut. After the intestines are out, the women have another job—separating all the small intestines from the large ones. (The lard between them is excellent for making soap with when dried out.) They can also empty the stomach, take the thin layer of skin off the inside, and put the emptied stomach in with the liverwurst. Then they should empty all the small intestines, turn them inside out, and scrape them. (Put a board in a pail of water, put the intestines on the board, and scrape with the back of a table knife.) This cleans the intestines and prepares them for use as sausage casings.

If pork chops are wanted, saw the carcass down the center of the backbone. If backbone and tenderloin are desired, chop off the ribs right next to the backbone all the way down on both sides. Carve off ribs, ham and bacon. To make good sausage, put in both shoulders, trimming off all the meat from the bone. (The bone can then be boiled and the rest of the meat picked off for liverwurst.) Trim all the fat and use the meat for sausages.

All the meat from the head, the legs from knees to hock, and the bones, as well as the stomach and tongue should be cooked until the meat is soft and can be easily picked off bones. The tongue must be scalded in hot water, and the outer skin be taken off. Then grind it all together. Cook the liver separately, but grind with the rest of the meat. Add enough of the broth that the meat was cooked in to the liverwurst, to make it fairly thin. Then cook it all on top of the stove, stirring frequently for about a half hour or more, until thick. Add salt and pepper to taste, put in cans and pressure cook for one hour.

Here is a way to sugar cure hams. The amounts are for a ham of about 25 lbs.

1 pint coarse salt
3 tablespoons brown sugar
2 tablespoons black pepper
1 tablespoon cayenne

Mix the ingredients, and lay ham on three or four thickness of paper. Newspaper works fine. Rub mixture on paper and rub rest over ham. Wrap tightly in paper, then cover with a white cloth such as an old bed sheet. Wrap tightly, and hang in basement or cool dark place, bone end down, for one month. When unwrapped, there may be a layer of mold over the outside of the ham. Trim mold off, and slice ham. Such a ham is good fried or boiled, and will keep for three or four months.

Meat Tenderizer
One metal face and one wooden one. No need to eat any more tough steak.
Price range: $5-$8

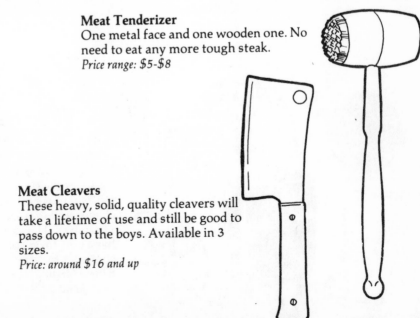

Meat Cleavers
These heavy, solid, quality cleavers will take a lifetime of use and still be good to pass down to the boys. Available in 3 sizes.
Price: around $16 and up

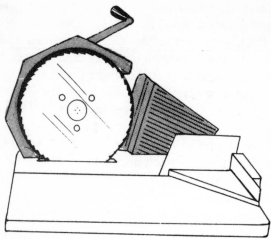

Meat Slicer

This rugged machine has a 6" blade that will handle all meat-slicing jobs. Food tray is big enough for roasts, breads and hams. Thumb guard and blade lock provide extra safety. Color finish.
Price range: $30-$40

Meat Grinders

Each moving part of these imported grinders is precision machined. The cast-iron housing is double hot-tin plated. Sturdy feet permit secure bolt fastening. Friction-free movement makes grinding and stuffing easy. Fat, muscle and meat are cut cleanly, can't slip through.

Each grinder comes with 2 forged-steel blade plates and a sausage funnel. This funnel, which attaches to the grinder, can save you the cost of a sausage stuffer.
model #5: grinds up to ½ lb. per minute, but is really too small for most jobs.
model #8: grinds up to 1½ lbs. per minute.
model #10: grinds up to 3 lbs. per minute. A good medium-sized all-purpose machine.
model #22: grinds up to 4 lbs. per minute. Very stable, with two pairs of feet for bolt fastening.
model #32: grinds up to 5 lbs. per minute. The 4" cylinder helps the home butcher work quickly and efficiently.
Price: $20 and up

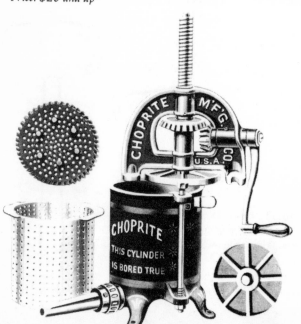

Sausage Stuffer and Lard Press

This is really three implements in one: it stuffs sausage casings, presses lard or cheese, and squeezes fruits and vegetables. The cast-iron construction has a non-toxic black finish. Includes container for straining lard. Capacity 8 qts. Height 22".
Price: $200-$225

11 | And The Baker

In pioneer days all the baking was done at home. Later, bakeries could only serve local customers. But with the coming of faster means of transportation, it all changed. At the turn of the century, about 95% of the bread consumed in North America was baked at home. Fifty years later, at least 95% of it was baked commercially. Baking bread had become big business. Today, bakeries across our country employ more workers than any other food industry.

In recent years, another revolution is taking place. Home baking is coming back. Quite simply, homemade bread tastes better, is more nutritious, and costs less.

We Changed Our Minds

When my husband and I were first married, we both agreed on the kind of bread we wanted–soft, fresh, white bakery bread. Now, thirteen years and eight children later, we are still agreed on the kind of bread we want. We both want tasty, nutritious, homemade, whole wheat bread.

Why the change? Because there was so much that bakery bread deprived us of. It never filled the kitchen with the tantalizing aroma of baking, which even the children enjoy and comment on. And we missed eating bread at its best–warm and crusty, straight from the oven. And who can put a money value on an honest compliment from the man of the house, "Mmm, what is better than a piece of Mom's good fresh bread!" Last, but not least, baking bread does save us money. Since many of us mothers cannot go out and be bread winners, we can be bread bakers, instead, and help the family economy in our own way.

—by Mrs. Martha Weaver

How I Learned to Enjoy Baking Bread

How well I remember my first bread-baking experience. I was not put to the task without warning, for my mother had told me that one of these days I was going to learn to make bread dough.

I can't explain why, but I dreaded the day when I would have to bake bread. Maybe it was because I often heard my sisters fuss about whose turn it was to bake–none of them wanted to. Maybe it was the tone of voice mother used when she talked to me about learning the art. At any rate, I developed a dislike for the task before I even tried it.

That memorable morning, Mother had combined the ingredients in the biggest dishpan available. The yeast had risen, and it was my job to mix in the flour and knead the dough with my hands. It was a big batch for our large, growing family and I was small for my twelve or thirteen years. It was an almost endless task. The dough had a gluey way of sticking to my fingers that I found unbearable. My shoulders ached, and I begged for someone to finish it for me. How was I ever going to get the smooth, elastic dough required for good bread? Mother told me this is the only way of learning, and to keep at it.

I worked for well over an hour before the dough was pronounced good enough, and I was released. For the rest of my girlhood days I slipped out of mixing the bread dough whenever I could, but my turn came every once in a while.

After I married, I found out that my husband was very fond of homemade bread. They seldom had any at home, and it was a treat for him. So I learned that love can make even bread-making a pleasant task. I tried my best to turn out nice golden loaves, which my husband praised for their softness.

I plan to pass on the art of bread-making to my little daughter, but I hope to do it differently from the way I learned it.

Here is the way I dream it will be:

One morning I will ask her if she wants to make a surprise for Dad. Of course, she will–children are always interested in making surprises. I will tell her how delighted Dad would be if she would make some soft, golden bread for his supper. We will be off to a happy start.

We will get two stainless steel mixing bowls both the same size. Each of us will need a big, strong spoon. I will put the ingredients in my bowl first and she will watch, and then do the same with hers.

First we will each put two cups of lukewarm water (105°F.) in our bowls. This is enough for just half of our usual batch, but I want it to be small so she can handle it better. Next we will add 2 tablespoons sugar and 2 teaspoons salt to the water and stir it well before sprinkling 2 teaspoons of yeast on the water.

We will have to let it sit undisturbed for 15 minutes or until the yeast is all dissolved and forms a foam on top of the water. Meanwhile we sift flour into a canister.

When the yeast is ready we will add 2 tablespoons lard or margarine to the mixture. Then we will be ready for the flour. At first we will stir in as much as we can. When the dough gets too stiff to stir with the spoon, we will make sure our hands are clean, and then start kneading with our hands. We will have to be careful not to add too much flour; for if we do, it will make the bread solid. But we will have to add enough to keep it from "sitting down." The dough will still feel sticky, but it will not cling to our hands as we knead it.

When the dough is soft, elastic, and pliable all the way through, we will make sure we have worked in all the stray dough that clings to the sides of the bowl. Then we will grease the bowl lightly and place the dough into it, turning the smooth side up. It will look like a smooth white ball. We will cover the bowl with a lid or a piece of plastic to keep the dough from drying out, and set it in a warm place, about 85°F.

After about 45 minutes, we will check to see if the dough has doubled in size. If it has, we will once more wash our hands and rub them with lard, then knead the dough a short while to get the air bubbles out. Again, we will grease the sides of the bowl lightly, place the dough into it, and set it back in its warm place to rise again.

The second time the dough has doubled in size, we will put it into bread pans. But first it must be divided into two portions and kneaded again. Placing the smooth side down, I will show my daughter how to knead the dough well after it is in the pans to get all the air bubbles out. Then we will turn the dough around with the smooth side up, and tuck down the ends to make a nice round loaf. The sides and bottom of the pan must be greased lightly, so the dough will not stick. Now we will set the pans back in a warm place, for the loaves must rise again before they are baked.

When the loaves have doubled in size, we will heat the oven to around 300° or 350°F and put in the bread. It will take about half an hour to bake. When the tops are a lovely brown, we will check to see if the loaves come out of the pans easily. If they do, we will take them out of the oven, remove them from the pans, and set them on a cloth or cooling rack. While they are still hot, we will brush the tops with butter, to keep the crust soft and pliable, and to improve the flavor. Although my daughter has watched me bake bread many times, I will explain the hows and whys of each step as we go.

While the bread is cooling on the table, Dad will come in. "Hmmm, all we need here is a knife and some butter and jelly," he will say, eyeing the loaves of bread.

My daughter will quickly bring the knife and butter and jelly, her eyes sparkling with the secret we share. I can tell she is saving it for the right time.

"Mmmmmmm, this hits the spot," Dad will say, taking the first bite. "Mother's homemade bread is hard to beat."

The right time has come. "I made the bread," she will say.

"You did!" Dad will exclaim. "Well, well. Now we have two bakers in the family. We should never run out of bread." He will pause to take another bite. "Baking bread is something you'll never be sorry you learned. You should be grateful that you have a mother who can teach you such useful things."

—by Mrs. Lester Graber

Recipe for Whole Wheat Bread

Step One: Put ¼ cup hot water in a cup. Add ½ teaspoon honey. Sprinkle 1 tablespoon yeast over the surface. Do not stir.

Step Two: Put 2¼ cups hot water in a mixing bowl. Add ¼ cup honey, ¼ cup cooking oil, 1½ tablespoons lecithin granules, 1 tablespoon salt, and 1 cup whey powder. Beat until ingredients have dissolved. Add 4 cups whole wheat flour. Stir until mixed well. Now stir in yeast mixture, which will by this time have risen to one cup.

Step Three: Repeat step one. Let yeast rise to one cup, then add to mixture. Stir.

Step Four: Add about four more cups of whole wheat flour; more or less may be needed. Just knead in flour until dough is a bit sticky, but not enough to stick to your fingers. Knead the dough until it feels smooth and elastic, about 10-15 minutes.

Step Five: Grease a clean bowl. Put the dough in it, and let it rise for one hour. Knead again, and let rise for another hour. Knead again, and form into loaves, placing them in bread pans. Let rise.

Step Six: Bake about one hour at 325° to 350°F. Makes three small loaves.

Bread Pan
A stainless-steel bread pan for the home baker. We only recently found this item, and tried it out in our oven. We were very impressed by the results. It bakes a good loaf and is easy to clean afterwards. Will last a lifetime.
Price: $4

Dough Mixer
We have to admit that most good Amish cooks have never heard of a dough mixer, let alone used one. Most just knead the dough with their bare hands. However, those who have tried this mechanical helper report that it does a good job. Besides, we sell a lot of them, so they must be working for someone. Double chrome-plated mixing rod and 12-qt. lifetime aluminum pail. Makes a bread batch from 2 to 8 loaves. Heavy cast working sections. Comes complete with instruction booklet and recipes.
Price range: $40-$50

Things I Want My Daughter To Know

—by Mrs. Ian Shantz

"The girls in town don't even know how to boil water," my doctor said. We were discussing the importance of teaching our children the skills of homemaking. His exasperated remark made me smile, and once again I vowed that mine would be taught all that we could possibly hand down to them. There are so many things a girl can learn.

I want my daughter to learn to stay at home. Beating the grocery store is quite a challenge, and the easiest way to do this is to be seldom found there. Naturally, with a large family, there are some items we need from the grocery store; but we try to send for them when Dad happens to be going to town anyhow. We rarely make an extra trip for groceries. Walking along the store aisles, viewing the variety of appetizing and handy items, who would not be tempted to buy this or that, which isn't really needed?

I want to teach my daughter to save. When the farm is paid for at last, we parents are inclined to think, "Now we don't have to be so careful anymore about what we spend." We take things home that we never allowed ourselves before. We forget that our children are just at the age when they should be learning to save. Will they be willing to start at the bottom as we did, when they start a home of their own, or will they consider where we left off just a beginning?

I want my daughter to learn to bake bread. After becoming used to homemade bread, our family does not find that spongy, store-bought stuff so very special. Baking bread is one of the skills all girls should learn. It does not take that much extra time, and it is certainly healthier.

There are some tricks to making bread. For a nicer texture in brown bread, add only enough flour to the liquid at first to make a soft dough like a cake dough. Before adding the remaining flour, let it stand a few hours, beating every half hour. This gives the whole wheat flour a chance to soak. I use over half whole wheat flour and finish it off with white. If honey is used instead of sugar, the bread will not be so crumbly. A few tablespoons of vinegar added to the dough helps to keep the bread moist longer.

I start the dough late in the afternoon. The school girls add the rest of the flour and work it after supper while I do the milking. Even the little boys enjoy punching bread dough. (Make sure their hands are clean, and don't be surprised if the dough lands on the floor when they get too eager!) By making the dough in the evening, you need very little yeast, so you save there, too.

Place the dough in a bowl with a plastic bag over it.

Set it in a cool place and let it rise overnight. The next morning it is ready to be punched down and placed in pans. Don't worry if the dough feels quite cool. The slower the process, the finer your bread will be. I often bake it the next afternoon after letting it rise slowly all morning. Oh, the delicious aroma that fills the room, and the satisfied feeling as I view the row of freshly baked loaves!

I want my daughter to learn to grow food in the garden. Many people buy coffee, but we consider it a luxury, as it is expensive and not even healthy. Instead, we grow our own herbs for teas. For years I've served home-grown tea to company, and have never heard a complaint. In fact, guests usually find it delicious, and give me compliments. There are many different kinds to choose from–peppermint, spearmint, comfrey, dill, clover, sage–the list could go on and on. For a mixed drink, add a little of each to your teapot, and enjoy a new flavor. If the herbs are dried, and stored in tight plastic bags, you can serve tea the year round.

I want my daughter to learn how to make cheese. We all know the high price of cheese, and how much a large family can consume. There are a variety of cheese recipes to try, but I find cheddar to be the least work and the type that I have the best luck with. Of course, I'm not enough of an expert to imitate the store cheese exactly; but with some practice, you can make cheese much like it. No expensive equipment is needed. The press I use is just a home-made affair with bricks for the weight on top.

In the fall, I make extra cheese to stock up for winter, as it's easier to make during warmer weather. When waxed, a cheese will keep for months, and the flavor and texture will improve with age.

I want my daughter to learn to make breakfast cereal. Our family enjoys homemade grapenuts and granola. We seldom buy cereal because I feel it lacks the nutritional value that homemade cereal has. And besides, it's a simple, daily example for the children that we don't have to depend on the store.

I want my daughter to learn how to help with butchering meats. Once a year our family has "butcher day." I can't deny that it's a long, hard day, but there is a feeling of accomplishment as we carry the fresh sausages, hams, bacons, liverwurst, and spare ribs to the cellar. Our parents taught us that nothing goes to waste, so even the meat scraps go into the kettle, mixed with lye, for making soap.

I want my daughter to learn how to make soap. Boiling soap has always fascinated me. I have many memories of watching my mother standing by the kettle, stirring the soap, happily absorbed in her work. I hope I can leave the same impressions with my daughters. Never are they to see me frown at certain jobs! Our attitude toward work can determine whether our children enjoy their tasks or not. Some say they hate the smell of boiling soap, but I've always thought it lovely. And to think that meat scraps can turn to smooth hard soap! (I have had flops, too, but that only adds to the excitement of getting up early in the morning to cut into the soap and see how it turned out.) We never buy dishwashing detergent, although I like to have a laundry powder on hand for badly soiled clothes.

Here's another hint to save on cleansers. To clean dirty wash basins and sinks, take an old rag and dip it in a little kerosene. Now wipe away the dirt. It works like magic.

I want my daughter to learn to make butter. We do not own a churn, but I sometimes let the children shake butter in a jar. I don't want them to be able to say in years to come that they never learned how to make butter!

I want my daughter to learn to sew. Have you ever tried to make the children's mitts instead of buying them? It's so simple, costs half the price, and they give longer wear. Even boys' caps and smocks are easy to make and so economical.

The list goes on and on. Of course we do all our canning–food out of tins is unheard of at our house. I hope I can teach canning skills to my daughters so they, too, can hand them on down.

We cannot live without the store altogether. But we can teach our children not to be dependent on it, by passing on to them the skills our mothers wanted us to learn.

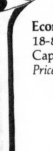

Economy Pitcher
18-8 stainless steel, with ice guard.
Capacity 2 qts.
Price: around $20

Bell-shaped Pitcher
18-8 stainless-steel, hollow handle.
Available with or without ice guard.
Capacity 2⅛ qts. A graceful yet practical
item much appreciated as a gift.
Price: around $35

Stainless Steel Pie Pan
We Amish must bake more pies than most, for these pans were specially manufactured for our people (and, we believe, are not available elsewhere). Practical, easy to clean, and long lasting. American-made of heavy stainless steel, they are very economical. We even use them as soup plates at the table.
Price: $3.50-$4.50

Stainless Steel Six-Bowl Set

This is one of our most popular items. Handy in the kitchen, and makes great gifts, too. The sizes included are: giant 13-qt. bowl, 8-qt. large mixing bowl., 5-qt., 3-qt., 1½ qt., and handy ¾ qt. bowls.
Price: around $35

Stainless Steel Three-Bowl Set

Three handy sized bowls. Easy to store, warm and last for years. Sizes are 3 qt., 1½ qt., and ¾ qt.
Price: under $10

Stainless Steel Stock Pots

Handy for cooking, canning and storing foods, as well as for soups and stocks. Seamless drawn, 18-8 stainless steel, commercial quality. Available in 3 sizes: 16-qt., 20-qt. and 24-qt.
Price: around $50 and up

Stainless Steel Pail

Handy 12-qt. economy model of 18-8 food-grade stainless steel.
Price range: $25-$30

Mortar and Pestle
Lacquered-finish hardwood
mortar and pestle for kitchen use
or as a decorator item. Diameter
3¾". Height 4¾".
Price: $10-$12

Stoneware Pantry Crocks
Perfect for pickles, sauerkraut,
and salt pork. Made in Canada by
Medalta Potteries. Can be
ordered with or without
stoneware lids. Four sizes in
stock, from 2 qts. to 3 gals. Sizes
up to 20 gals. available on special
order.
*The 2-gal. crock without lid is priced
around $20.*

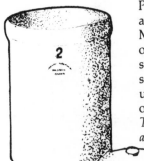

Stoneware Ice Cooler
This unique item comes
complete with nickel-plated
spigot. Stoneware is a
wonderful insulator.
Perfect for iced tea, fruit
juice, or lemonade.
Price range: $50-$60

Bean Pot
Hand-glazed earthenware with
tight-fitting lid. Color is attractive
natural brown. Doubles as a
cookie jar. Diameter 9½".
Height 5".
Price range: $12-$15

White Mountain Popcorn Maker
Flat-bottomed, thin-steel cooking pot with internal, hand-cranked wiper blade to churn up the kernels. The popped kernels rise to the top, while the unpopped ones sift down to the bottom to be popped. Simple, slow cranking action gives perfect kernels every time.
Price: $20-$25

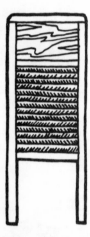

Daughter-Size Washboard
Neatly constructed with back drain, this is very serviceable for light washing. However, it is mainly a nostalgic item to remind people of a better era when women weren't afraid of hard work. Measures 17" x 8½".
Price range: $8-$12

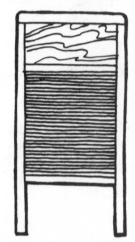

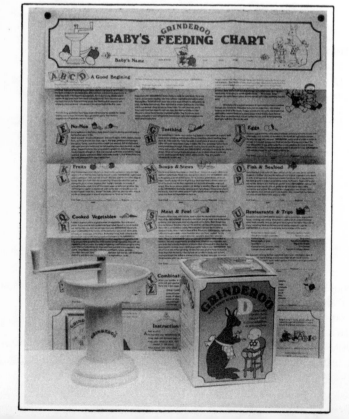

Grandma's Economy Washboard
Comes complete with back drain and standard-size rubbing surface. Very serviceable. Overall size 23" x 12½".
Price range: $10-$15

Baby Food Grinder
Quick and easy to use. Handy to take on trips. Grinderoo pays for itself in just a couple of weeks by replacing costly commercial baby foods. Dishwasher safe, may be sterilized. Stainless steel blade and strainer. Lemon-yellow color. Includes colorful box and baby feeding chart.
Price: under $10

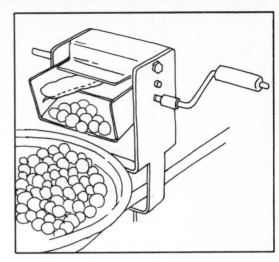

Pea Sheller

A small, efficient sheller for blackeyed,
purple hulls and cream peas. Also good
for butter beans if they are fresh and
ripe. Does not damage vegetables. Can be
motorized by attaching to a hand mixer.
Price: around $20

Bean Chopper

Turn the handle and beans
are perfectly chopped by 3
revolving, stainless-steel
cutter blades. Ideal for
canning or freezing. Heavy
cast iron. Weight 2½ lbs.
Price: around $25

Vegetable Steamer

Steam cook foods to retain
full natural flavors. Perfect
for vegetables, meats and
fish. Foods are cooked
tender, not soggy, burned
or scorched. Adjusts to any
pot size. Has lift-out
handles, and folds to store.
Stainless steel.
Price: under $5

Bean Slicer

Cuts lengthwise or French
style. Great time saver,
perfect for freezing or
canning. Heavy cast iron
with six steel cutting
blades. Weight 2½ lbs.
Price: around $27

Kernel Kutter

Cut whole kernel corn without mashing
or crushing. For cooking, relishes,
freezing or creamed corn. Fit flexible
saw-toothed cutter on the ear, and push
down. Stainless steel cutting blade,
plastic-coated handles. Length 10".
Price: under $5

13 | Through the Mill

They used to say that if a man cut his own firewood, it would warm him twice: once when he cut it, and again when he burned it. The same can be said for grinding your own flour and cereal: they taste better, not only because they are fresher, but because you have worked up an appetite in the process.

Corona Metal Burr Mill

This is the same as the King Convertible, but without stone plates. Will grind 1 lb. of cereal per minute to obtain fine flour without the stone burrs; you would have to run the grain through the mill several times.

Price range: $35-$45

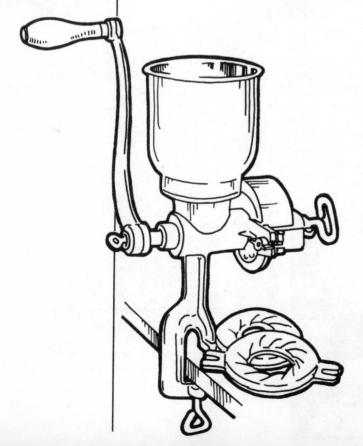

Corona King Convertible

Our most popular mill, with interchangeable metal and stone plates. Adjusts from coarse to fine grind. Will mill any dry grain. Stones are manufactured especially for the Corona and have a special bonding to prevent flaking. Made of a petrified carbon material that will last a lifetime. Will grind fine flour in one operation without heating problems, but not designed for operating at more than 150 rpm.

Use the metal plate to crack grain or grind moist items. Use stone plates for grinding flour. Changing metal plates or stones is quick and easy.

Mill comes with a high hopper. It is accurately machined, and made of durable, cast-iron parts. The electro-tinned finish guarantees a sanitary, easy-to-clean, rust-proof utensil.

The Corona King Convertible is recommended by *Harrowsmith* magazine.

Price range: $75-$85

Poppy Seed Mill
A quality machine imported from
Romania. Grinds poppy seeds, pepper,
salt or coffee. Sturdy clamp on base
Attractive red and yellow finish.
Price range: $15-$20

Old-Fashioned Coffee Mill
This is a quality mill. Both its metal and
wooden parts are made from the same
pattern used to make the original ones
years ago. This is not a reproduction, it's
the same product: a new antique!
Price: $40-$45

How To Cheat the Grocery Man

14

Home-made Breakfast Cereals

When they think of breakfast cereal, most people picture Corn Flakes, Wheaties, Shreddies, Kelloggs, General Mills, colorful boxes, promotional gimmicks, free trinkets, and winning a trip to the Bahamas. They also think, with a shiver, of staring at this all through breakfast for most of their lives; in Canada they can even read all about it in two languages.

Our family has escaped the morning grip of the cereal makers, simply by making our own. We call it grapenuts, but it bears little resemblance in taste, appearance or price to the grapenuts you buy at the supermarket.

Preparing grapenuts at our house is a three-step procedure. First Mom bakes the grapenut cakes in our wood-burning kitchen range. This cake is good to eat in itself, although it has a heavy, solid texture.

Next we rub the cooled cake through a grapenut screen, which reduces it to uniform-sized crumbs. Mom keeps the cake handy and watches for her chance. If I or the children are unemployed during the evening hours, or sitting and talking with a visitor during the day, she will appear with the pan of grapenut cake and the screen. She figures we might as well be using our hands while we talk.

The third step is to dry the crumbs. This is done by spreading them in shallow pans and placing them in the oven of the kitchen range or on top of the heating stove. In either case we use heat already being produced, so it costs us nothing.

Surprisingly enough, we are willing to break the breakfast cereals tradition, and share the recipe for home made grapenuts with anyone who orders a five-pound sample pack.

The history of breakfast cereal is as colorful as the boxes it is marketed in. In the late 1800s, Dr. John H. Kellogg was looking for a better breakfast idea. He was responsible for the diet of more than 1200 patients at his health sanitarium in Battle Creek, Michigan. (He was also responsible for the diet of the 1800 attendants who cared for his pampered patients.)

One day, a lady patient told Dr. Kellogg about a machine that made a soft wheat cereal. It was the invention of a man named Henry Perkey of Denver, Colorado. Dr. Kellogg immediately travelled to Denver to see the machine and talk with its inventor. The machine was simple enough–it pressed cooked wheat between two rollers. One roller was smooth and the other had fine grooves. The resulting threads of wheat paste were then folded into pillow-shaped biscuits.

Impressed by what he saw, Dr. Kellogg bargained with Perkey for his machine. At first Perkey agreed to bring it to Battle Creek, but after Kellogg left he had second thoughts, and decided to go into business for himself, instead. Perkey chose Niagara Falls as the best place to set up business. There he could introduce his new cereal to honeymooners ready to set up housekeeping.

Setting the trend for future cereal makers, he advertised it aggressively with greater emphasis on sales than on honesty: "Stomach comfort in every shred. Millions of persons are unable to properly digest starch. What the sufferer needs is food, not medicine. Shredded Whole Wheat, made by the Natural Food Company."

It was an immediate success. Soon word reached Battle Creek. Dr. Kellogg, angry and disappointed, made a second attempt. He offered $100,000 for the machine and the patent, but Perkey refused.

In desperation, John Kellogg returned to Battle Creek, and set up his own cereal factory. He designed his machine differently to avoid patent infringement; but his version didn't work as well, so he called on his younger brother, William Keith, to give him a hand.

Soon William Keith had most of the problems under control, which created new ones. He was no longer willing to take orders from his older brother. A dispute over paying for some new machinery led to a lawsuit between the brothers. (Ironically, both were very religious and staunch believers in non-violence. Neither of them would have harmed a rabbit. But when money was involved, they were at each other's throats.)

The courts favored the younger brother, and he won control of the factory. Today, the name of W.K. Kellogg is a household word throughout North America. But the battle was not yet over. The treatment W.K. had given his older brother was to be returned in kind, by a complete stranger.

Charles W. Post arrived on the scene with the invention of Postum, a non-coffee drink aimed at health-conscious people. Soon Postum was off to a healthy start, and Charles decided to enter the now-booming breakfast-cereal business. He put a new cereal on the market which he called Grape Nuts. It was a marvel indeed–recommended for fighting tuberculosis, loose teeth, and malaria. It was better than surgery for appendicitis, and was even said to be good brain food.

In 1906, the Pure Food and Drug Act prohibited such fraudulent claims, but Post could still suggest its wonderful qualities by simply repeating on every box, "There's A Reason!"

In view of the claims of other cereal makers, both past and present, what can we say about our cereal? As far as we know, it will not cure tuberculosis, malaria, appendicitis or loose teeth.

We suspect it does nothing for the brain. We don't add vitamins. We don't hide trinkets at the bottom of the box. We don't stage contests or give free coupons for foods that are still ridiculously expensive after the value of the coupon has been deducted.

All we claim is that our family enjoys homemade grapenuts every morning for breakfast. We thrive on it. Sometimes one of our five boys will turn down an egg or an orange, but rarely his bowl of grapenuts. We are prepared to sell you a five-pound introductory pack at a reasonable price. Along with the sample, we will send you recipes and complete instructions so you can make your own grapenuts if you prefer that to reordering from us.

We may not make a fortune under such an arrangement. But when we consider the lives of those who went before us in the cereal business, making a fortune doesn't seem particularly attractive. Riches caused Charles Post to divorce his faithful wife, who had labored unselfishly at his side to make his business a success. He married his secretary, who was twenty years younger than he was. But in the end, all the health-giving properties of Postum and Grape Nuts failed to keep their manufacturer well. Post developed a severe stomach ailment, and went to the Mayo Clinic for diagnosis. The doctors' verdict so depressed him that he committed suicide after commanding that his body be buried under seven feet of concrete in Oak Hill Cemetery.

Meat that Never Moved a Muscle

There is no doubt that meat is one of the best sources of the nutrition and protein our bodies need. But unfortunately, meat is expensive, as large amounts of grain and plant food are required to produce a pound of meat.

Textured Vegetable Protein (TVP) is a soy-bean product with roughly the equivalent protein of meat at a fraction of the cost. TVP has been used commercially for several years by food processors and institutions such as hospitals, orphanages and schools. However, it has not been readily available to housewives except in the form of imitation bacon bits.

In our experience, TVP is an ideal meat extender. It has almost no taste of its own, but, as it cooks, it absorbs the taste of any food to which it is added. The texture is fibrous and chewy, almost impossible to distinguish from meat. The amount of TVP added to meat can vary: you can add up to 50% or more before you can taste the difference, even when samples are compared with unextended meat.

TVP is sold in dehydrated form as dry granules, and mixed with two parts liquid to one part TVP. Either water or milk can be used as liquid.

The use of TVP is a good way to cut down on the grocery bill, without compromising either taste or nutrition. With meat costing one, two or even three dollars a pound at the supermarket, TVP is a real bargain at under 25¢ a pound.

We have TVP available in bulk 20 kg bags only; but it has a good shelf life, especially if stored in air-tight containers, such as lard cans or plastic pails with covers. (Price range: $45)

Food Storage

It is common knowledge that most of our population centers have only enough food to feed their people for a week or ten days, should supplies be cut off. That certainly is not an ideal arrangement. Nothing as basic as food should be left so vulnerable to disruption.

We feel the best solution is to grow and process our own food as far as possible; raising livestock, gardening, canning, etc. Although we are far from self-sufficient on our farm, if no new supplies were permitted to enter and nothing was permitted to leave, we still would not starve in the foreseeable future.

It is hardly likely that everyone concerned about food supply will immediately set up in a farm setting. However, such people may consider dried food specially packaged in inert gas for long-term storage. (People report that such food has kept up to twelve years.)

Buying a year's supply of dried food is not a bad investment from any viewpoint. Food prices are going up, and money is going down. Dried foods are easy to store: enough for one person for a year can be stored under a bed as dehydrated foods are one quarter the size and approximately one tenth the weight of regular canned goods. Dried foods are easy to prepare; just add water, and most dried foods can be cooked and prepared in minutes. Many can also be eaten in the dry form as delicious snacks.

Tasty and colorful, our dried foods are appetizing in appearance and nutritional. No refrigeration is needed, yet food will not be harmed by freezing. Only top quality foods are used; fruits and vegetables are harvested when they are ripe. There is no waste, as the foods have been cleaned, peeled and trimmed. They are ready to use.

Many canoeists, campers, hikers and backpackers like these foods, which they repack into plastic zip bags, and save money over prepackaged camp foods.

Our basic one-year unit has a shipping weight of approximately 330 lbs. and requires approximately $10\frac{1}{2}$ cu. ft. storage. Packed in no. 10 tins (100 liquid oz. size), it contains the following: Basic One-Year Unit. (Price range: $600-$700)

Protein:

1 tin Powdered Cheddar Cheese
1 tin Beef Base
1 tin Chicken Base
6 tins White Beans
18 tins Skim Milk Powder
6 tins Simulated Beef Granules (TVP)
1 tin Simulated Bacon Chips (TVP)

Vegetables:

1 tin Sweet Corn Kernels
1 tin Tomato Flakes
6 tins Potato Granules
1 tin Carrots
2 tins 7-Mixed Vegetables (soup mix)
1 tin Green Garden Peas
1 tin Onion Flakes

Grain:

4 tins Long Grain Rice
4 tins Oatmeal
11 tins Cracked Wheat

Fruit:

2 tins Apple Chips
2 tins Apple Granules
2 tins Mixed Fruit

Let There Be Light

15

(Not available from The Pioneer Place)

As we have no electricity, every Amish household depends heavily on kerosene or gas lamps. In this catalogue we are not listing any of the standard wick-and-burner type lamps, although they are used by many of our families. We have two reasons for leaving them out. First, this type of lamp is available, or rapidly becoming so, in nearly every hardware and department store. Second, all our lamps must be sent through the mail, and we fear that some postal workers derive great pleasure from the sound of tinkling glass fragments. So, instead, we are listing the Leacock pressure reading lamp, and various Aladdin lamps.

The Leacock Lamp
Designed and manufactured by Amishman Levi Esh, this lamp is available in wall or table model, with glass or fibreglass shade, and with a baked-enamel or chrome finish. This lantern burns under pressure, holds a good supply of fuel, produces a bright, white light with either kerosene or naphtha. All burner parts are interchangeable with those for Coleman lamps, so repairs can be made easily with readily available materials.

We use one of these lamps every day in our home, and would hate to have to do without it.
Price range: $75-$100

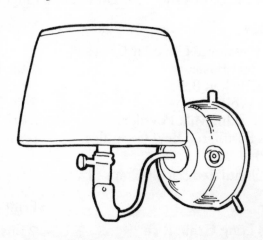

Aladdin Lamps

Famous for quality for many years, Aladdin lamps have been used and loved the world over. The light produced is not as bright as that of the Leacock, but there is also no hissing sound as there is with a pressure lamp. These lamps give very satisfactory service, but they should not be turned too high or they will smoke.

Aladdin lamps have all the warmth and beauty of traditional design; they are both practical and decorative. Every model features Aladdin's unique incandescent mantle and kerosene burner assembly. The brilliant white light produced can be safely adjusted up to the equivalent of a 60-watt bulb without smoking. Safe and odorless, the lamps require no pumping. Burn approx. 50 hrs. per gal. of kerosene. Following are several types.

Brass Table Lamp

Comes complete with mantle and burner. Shade must be ordered separately. The brass table lamp pictured here has a Glass Century shade, which is described later in the chapter.

Price: $65-$75 (without shade)

Glass Table Lamp

Introduced in 1939, the "Lincoln Drape" design is reproduced on heavy amber glass. Beautiful with or without a shade, it can be fitted with any of the shades we list.

Price: $60-$65 (without shade)

Aluminum Table Lamp

A sensible, practical lamp at a reasonable price. It is pictured here with a parchment shade, but any of our shades will fit it. It can also be used without a shade.

Price: $50-$55 (without shade)

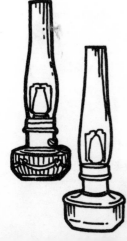

Shelf Lamp

Sturdy, lightweight and portable, these lamps are perfect for cabins, patios, etc. They are also dependable protection against a power failure. The lamp comes in either a glass or aluminum model. A shade is not recommended, as the extra weight can unbalance the lamp, and cause it to tip over.

Price: $45-$50

Accessories for Aluminum Shelf Lamp

Hanger: This will convert the shelf lamp into a hanging lamp, allowing the addition of a shade. It is pictured here with a parchment shade, but the shade is not included. *Price: $15-$20*

Wall Bracket: This will convert a free-standing shelf lamp to a wall-mounted lamp to allow the addition of a shade. It is pictured here with a parchment shade, but the shade must be ordered separately. *Price: $10-$15*

Caboose Bracket: This adjustable, heavy-duty, double-action wall bracket has a shock-absorbing spring that makes it nice for campers or motor homes. It is still used in rail yard cabooses throughout the world. *Price: $25*

We sell four types of shade. Each comes with a tripod, so there is no need to order one separately. However, please be sure to tell us what model lamp the shade is for, so we can supply the correct tripod.

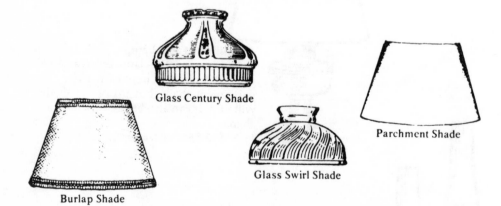

Glass Century Shade

Parchment Shade

Glass Swirl Shade

Burlap Shade

Parchment shade. *Price: $16*
Burlap shade. *Price: $18*
Glass Swirl shade. Available in red, green or white. *Price: $50*
Glass Century shade. Available in opal, white, violet, dogwood, rose and crystal champagne. *Price: $40*

The Comforts of Home

16

A Special Chair

When my wife and I married more than ten years ago, we gathered together whatever furniture we felt we needed to set up housekeeping. But one missing item left our home incomplete–we lacked a hickory rocking chair. Both of us had grown up in homes where a handmade chair of bent hickory always stood in the living room, and we felt our home needed such a chair, too.

There was nothing unusual in this, for the Amish home that does not have at least one rocking chair of bent hickory is rare, indeed. So most young couples, when they marry, do exactly what we did–put a bent hickory rocker high on the list of items to buy.

But where would we get one? These chairs are built only in Amish communities; and Canada, with a very small population of our people, had no chair-maker. We finally ended up importing a chair from my wife's childhood community, Wayne County, Ohio.

We liked the chair immediately, and the longer we have it, the more we like it. When visitors come to our house, we offer them the rocking chair; but when no visitors are here, we use it ourselves. It has rocked all our children, and if we live and the world stands, we hope it will rock our grandchildren.

Several years ago it became obvious that our community needed its own chair maker. Importing chairs from the U.S. wasn't any good. John Martin accepted the challenge. He traveled to Amish chair shops in Pennsylvania and Ohio for on-the-job training. He then set up his shop and went back to work.

Almost immediately he ran into a production snag–he could not find enough hickory sprouts with which to build the chairs. The local supply was scant and hard to find. He asked the Ministry of Natural Resources if they knew where stands of Shagbark Hickory grew, as he wanted to cut some sprouts. It was like asking the bank manager if he knew of any safes to crack. John was informed that it is illegal to cut sprouts in Ontario.

An uncle in Iowa heard of John's plight and came to the rescue. There were lots of hickory sprouts in Iowa; in fact, they were growing like weeds all over his farm. John was welcome to all he could cut.

Iowa hickory sprouts have been used to build Ontario chairs ever since.

When we first offered these chairs several years ago, it was the first time they were available to Canada's non-Amish population. The response has been gratifying–we have shipped chairs everywhere from Newfoundland to the Yukon.

Our chair-maker is pleased, of course, and his venture is successful in every aspect except one. He is so busy that he has no time to relax in the chairs he builds!

Cedar Chests

These are solid cedar chests, made of Tennessee aromatic red cedar. They have been used by Amish families for years, so we know they stand up under the stress and strain of large families. We have never heard of anyone being disappointed in one of these chests. Order one for yourself or for someone you love; they make gifts that are both beautiful and practical, and will last for years.

All the chests we list are kits, which means they are shipped disassembled and unfinished. But everything you need to assemble them is included. Assembly time is from three to four hours.

The prices vary, of course, depending on the model and size. The cheapest ones start around $150, the more expensive ones around $250.

Amish Quilts

The auctioneer seemed to gain momentum and enthusiasm as the bidding continued. "I have twelve hundred and fifty dollars. Who will give me twelve seventy-five, anywhere, seventy . . ."

It was a warm spring day in 1978, at the annual Mennonite Central Committee relief sale in New Hamburg, Ontario. The auctioneer was selling handmade quilts that had been brought to the sale by Mennonite and Amish ladies. The bidding continued, and this particular quilt was finally knocked down at the record-breaking price of $1300.

Two ladies, Elizabeth and Eva Slaubaugh, have offered to supply us with quilts. They have been making quilts for years, and have a reputation for exact, neat and painstaking work.

It takes a lot of time and work to make a quilt, so our supply will be extremely limited, and you may have to wait several months for yours to be finished. But if you are interested in hand-stitched quilts, write to us for information and prices on various patterns and sizes. If you have a particular pattern you would like to have custom made, let us know.

Quilt prices will vary quite a bit, depending on the size and pattern required; but all will be considerably less than the record-breaking quilt sold at New Hamburg! Most quilts will be priced somewhere between $300 and $600.

Our Amish Publishing House

Our community operates a religious publishing house. We publish a number of casebound books, including a values series of reading textbooks for elementary schools, Grades 1 to 8.

We also publish three monthly magazines, which have a

circulation of about 13,000. The *Blackboard Bulletin* is a paper promoting Christian day schools; the *Young Companion* is directed at young people, and *Family Life* is a family paper. Although all our material is written and edited with the needs of the plain people in mind, we do have many subscribers who enjoy our papers, who are neither Mennonite nor Amish.

For sample copies of all three magazines, send us two dollars and a note of your name and address.

Bent Hickory Rocking chair
Unique, old-fashioned, homey and comfortable, these durable chairs will last for generations. Guaranteed to please. Each chair is individually handcrafted, so no two are exactly alike.
Adult chairs, postpaid in Canada, price $130 and up

Cushions and Chair-back Covers
These cushions and chair-back covers are specially hand quilted by ladies in our community.
Price: $50 and up.

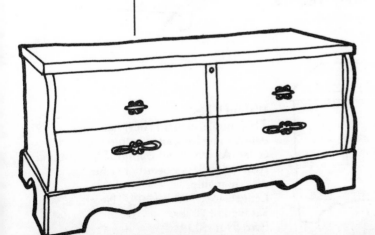

"Early American" Cedar Chest
Beautiful solid cedar chest with bright brass hardware. Length 46¾". Width 20⅜". Height 20½". Kit weight: 70 lbs.
Price: $200-$225

A large family may need assorted sizes of cedar chests. These three are identical, except for size. All come complete with hardware.

Medium Junior
Length 35". Width 16¼". Height 15".
Kit weight 38 lbs.
Price: $150-$160

Junior
Length 41¼". Width 18¾". Height 17½".
Kit weight 51 lbs.
Price: $160-$175

Senior
Length 46¾". Width 20⅜". Height 20½".
Kit weight 70 lbs.
Price: $175-$185

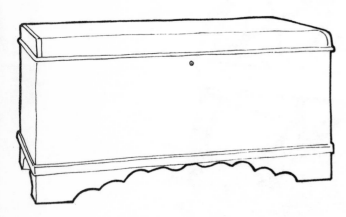

"Waterfall" Cedar Chest
The "Waterfall" chest is very attractive. It has a roll and scalloped base.
Length 46¾". Width 20⅜". Height 21¾".
Kit weight 70 lbs.
Price: $175-$190

Tot's Cedar Chest
This small chest provides privacy for a child's toys and treasures. Also ideal for underclothing and socks. Complete with hardware.
Length 19½". Width 8½". Height 8".
Kit weight 10 lbs.
Price: $40-$50

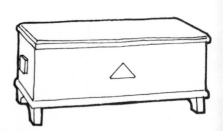

Walnut Chest
This simple, elegant chest has 5-ply panels. The back and bottom are solid cedar. All trim solid walnut. The diamond front adds classic beauty to fine workmanship.
Length 46¾". Width 20¾". Height 20½".
Kit weight 70 lbs.
Price: $210-$230

Index

Apple Parer, White Mountain,   44

Baby Food Grinder,   92
Bean Chopper,   93
Bean Pot,   91
Bean Slicer,   93
Bells,   59-60
  Farm Bell,   59
  Post Bell,   59
  School Bells,   60
  Ship's Bell,   60
  Steer Head Bell,   60
Birdhouses,   39-41
  Perch, Martin House,   41
  Post, Telescoping Mounting,   41
  Post, Heavy-duty 3-Section,   41
  Socket, Mounting-post,   41
  Trio-Castle, 24-family,   41
  Trio-Grandma, 8-family,   40
  Trio-Grandpa, 12-family,   41
  Trio-Musselman, 12-family,   40
  Trio-Wade, 12-family,   40
Bottle Capper,   75
Bottle Crowns,   75
Bowl Set, Six Stainless Steel,   90
Bowl Set, Three Stainless Steel,   90
Brackets,   102
  Caboose,   102
  Hanger,   102
  Wall,   102
Bread Pan,   86
Buggies,   26-27
  Amish Open Buggy,   26
  Amish Surrey,   27
  Two Seater Carriage,   27
Butter Mold,   58
Butter Paddles,   58
Butter Parchments,   58

Canners, 79
  Pressure, 79
  Steam, 79
Canning Jars, 76
Cheese Press, 55
Cherry Pitter, White Mountain, 76
Cherry Stoner, Chop-Rite, 76
Chests, 105-106
  Early American Cedar, 105
  Junior, 106
  Medium Junior, 106
  Senior, 106
  Tot's Cedar, 106
  Walnut, 106
  Waterfall Cedar, 106
Churn, Daisy, 57
Churn, Dasher, 58
Cider Press, The Pioneer Place, 44
  Metal Parts Kit, 44
Coffee Mill, Old-fashioned, 95
Collars, 29
  Buggy, 29
  Draft Horses, 29
  Pony, 29
  All-steel Double-tree, 29
Cook Stove, The Pioneer Maid, 66
Copper Wash Boiler, 78
Corn Sheller, The Bell, 32
Corona King Convertible, 94
Corona Metal Burr Mill, 94
Cream Separator, 57
Crock, Stoneware Pantry, 91
Cultivator, Garden, 31
Cushions and Chair-back Covers, 105
Cylinders, Brass-lined, 22

Dough Mixer, 86

Grinder, Baby Food, 92
Grinder, Meat, 82

Harnesses, 28
  Double Buggy, 28
  Double Pony, 28
  Farm Team, 28
  Single Buggy, 28
  Single Pony, 28
Hickory Rocking Chair, 105
Hoes, Old-country, 32

Ice Cooler, Stoneware, 91
Ice Cream Freezer, White Mountain, 54

Jars, Traditional Canning,   76
Juicer,   78

Kernel Kutter,   93

Lamps,   100-102
  Aladdin,   101
  Aluminum Table,   101
  Brackets,   102
  Brass Table,   101
  Glass Table,   101
  Shades,   102
  Shelf,   101
Lard Press and Sausage Stuffer,   82

Meat Cleaver,   81
Meat Grinder,   82
Meat Slicer,   82
Meat Tenderizer,   81
Mills,   94-95
  Burr, Corona Metal,   94
  Coffee, Old-fashioned,   95
  Convertible, Corona King,   94
  Poppy Seed,   95

Pail, Stainless Steel,   90
Pea Sheller,   93
Pestle & Mortar,   91
Pie Pan, Stainless Steel,   89
Pitchers,   89
  Bell-shaped,   89
  Economy,   89
Popcorn Maker, White Mountain,   92
Poppy Seed Mill,   95
Pots, Stainless Steel Stock,   90
Pressure Canner,   79
Pumps,   21-22
  Iron Pitcher,   21
  Pump Jack,   22
  Windmill Force, Model 50A,   21

Rocking Chair, Bent Hickory,   105

Sausage Stuffer and Lard Press,   82
Seeder, Garden,   32
Shades, Lamp,   102
  Burlap,   102
  Glass Century,   102
  Glass Swirl,   102
  Parchment,   102
Shafts,   29
Sheller, Pea,   93

Sparrow Trap, 42
Steam Canner, 79
Steamer, Vegetable, 93
Stock Pots, Stainless Steel, 90
Strainer, Victorio, 77
   Berry Screen, 77
   Grape Spiral, 77
   Pulley Shaft, 77
   Pumpkin Screen, 77

Vegetable Steamer, 93
Victorio Strainer, 77
   Parts, 77

Washboards, 92
   Daughter-size, 92
   Grandma's Economy, 92
Wheels, Buggy, 28
Windmill, 22
   Brass-lined Cylinders, Model a/40, 22

The prices listed in this catalogue are only approximate. For a current price list and ordering instructions, address your request to: The Pioneer Place, Route 4, Aylmer, Ontario, Canada N5H 2R3. There is no charge for the price list, but be sure to include your name and complete mailing address. Please print or type.